The Gun Digest Book of

FIREARMS ASSEMBLY/ DISASSEMBLY

PART IV
CENTERFIRE RIFLES

by J.B. Wood

DBI Books, Inc.

Editorial Staff:

Editor
Harold A. Murtz
Graphic Design
MacDonald Graphics
Cover Illustration
James M. Triggs
Associate Publisher
Sheldon L. Factor

To George P. Whittington, *B'wana m'kubwa*—and Agnes, of course

Acknowledgements

My thanks to these people, who helped to make this book possible—

John S. Yarger, John A. Yarger, James W. Yarger, and Larry McClarney of Lock & Load Gun Shop, Glenn Lancaster, Al Paulsen, Brian Paulsen, Maurice Paulsen, Dr. Kenneth M. Eblen, Earle G. Harrington of Savage Arms, Alan Carver of Browning, Jack Sharry of Harrington & Richardson, Larry K. Goodstal of Remington, Harold A. Murtz, Ray Diekmann, George P. Whittington, Carl Bonnell and Jesse Smith of Sportsman's Corner, George Klutey, James S. Priest III, Grover Toalson, W. H. Wood, Marvin Dill, Tony Babbs, and A. D. Jenkins.

ISBN 0-695-81420-5   Library of Congress Catalog Card # 79-54271

CONTENTS

Introduction 4

A Note on Reassembly 5

Tools 6

British SMLE No. 1, MKIII 11

Browning BAR 19

Japanese Arisaka Type 99 29

Marlin 336 37

Mauser 1898 45

Mosin-Nagant 53

Mossberg 479 61

Remington Model 8 70

Remington 600 79

Remington 700 85

Remington 742 91

Remington 760 104

Remington 788 114

Remington Rolling Block 121

Ruger 44 Carbine 129

Ruger Mini-14 142

Ruger No. 1 150

Ruger 77 159

Sako Forester 167

Savage 99 174

Savage 110 184

Savage 340 192

Schmidt-Rubin 1911 200

U.S. Krag-Jorgensen 208

U.S. Model 1917 Enfield 215

U.S. M-1 Carbine 222

U.S. M-1 Garand 230

U.S. Springfield 1903 239

Weatherby Mark V 246

Winchester 70 253

Winchester 71 261

Winchester 1892 270

Winchester 1894 280

INTRODUCTION

There are only three good reasons for taking a rifle completely apart: For repair, for refinishing, or for in-depth cleaning. The non-professional will usually avoid the first two reasons, but I have seen some gruesome exceptions. The last one, though, is a legitimate motive for the gun owner to decide on trying total takedown. Many gunsmiths are so busy with repair work that routine cleaning jobs may be postponed for some time. So, the do-it-yourself approach may be the only way to get it done without a lengthy wait.

With some guns, though, those not familiar with the internal mechanism may find that they have real problems. If they have the original manual or instruction sheet, this will help up to a point, but these usually go only as far as field-stripping. The manuals for some of the older guns are valuable items, and not commonly available. Some of the imported guns have direct-translation manuals that are good for a laugh, but useless otherwise. This book, like the others in the series, was designed to fill this gap in firearms information. Volumes I and II covered pistols and revolvers, and Volume III covered rimfire rifles. Volume V will cover shotguns.

With the right instructions, a very knowledgeable amateur can usually manage total takedown and reassembly, but he must have some mechanical aptitude. There are some points that may require the tools and skills of the gunsmith. This book is intended for both the amateur and the professional, and even the simpler operations are described and illustrated.

Several of the tools required are not usually found on the local hardware counter, so a section on tools is included, along with the sources and prices, when available.

When taking any gun apart, there are a few general rules which should be followed. Although a tight assembly may require a light tap with a plastic mallet, never use extreme force. Wear safety glasses at all times, to shield the eyes from spring-powered parts. Don't dismantle a gun over surfaces that may lose small parts, such as tall grass or shag rugs. Before you start, read the instructions all the way through.

Everyone knows, of course, that the first disassembly step is to remove the cartridges, so I won't repeat this at the start of each set of instructions. I'll say it once, right now: *Before you start to take any gun apart, be sure that it is entirely unloaded*. Don't rely on the mechanism—*look* inside. Some guns can "hide" a round in the magazine system.

The *Gun Digest Book of Exploded Firearms Drawings,* also available from DBI Books, Inc., would be a good companion to this book, as it shows parts relationships for more than 300 guns.

J. B. Wood
Raintree House
Corydon, Kentucky
April, 1980

A Note on Reassembly

Most of the rifles covered in this book can be reassembled by simply reversing the order of disassembly, carefully replacing the parts in the same manner they were removed. In a few instances, special instructions are required, and these are listed with each gun under "Reassembly Tips." In certain cases, reassembly photos are also provided.

If there are no special instructions or photos with a particular gun, you may assume that it can just be reassembled in reverse order. During disassembly, note the relationship of all parts and springs, and lay them out on the workbench in the order they were removed. By following this procedure you should have no difficulty.

TOOLS

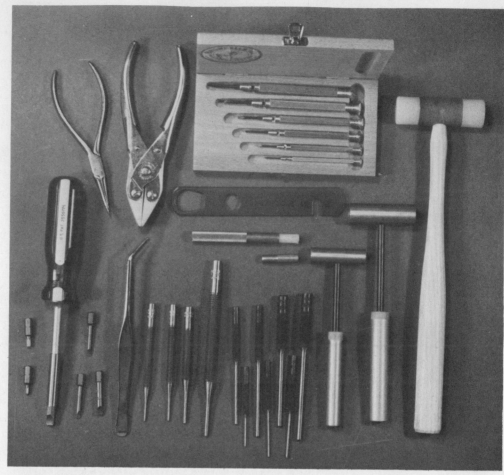

Countless firearms, old and new, bear the marks, burrs, and gouges that are the result of using the wrong tools for taking them apart. In the interest of preventing this sort of thing, I am including here a group of tools that are the best types for the disassembly of rifles. Except for the few shop-made tools for special purposes, all of those shown here are available from one of these three sources.

Brownells, Inc.
Route 2, Box 1
Montezuma, Iowa 50171

B-Square Company
P.O. Box 11281
Forth Worth, Texas 76109

Williams Gun Sight Company
7389 Lapeer Road
Davison, Michigan 48423

General Instructions:

Screwdrivers: Always be sure the blade of the screwdriver **exactly** fits the slot in the screw head, both in thickness and in width. If you don't have one that fits, grind or file the tip until it does. You may ruin a few screwdrivers, but better them than the screws on a fine rifle.

Slave pins: There are several references in this book to slave pins, and some non-gunsmith readers may not be familiar with the term. A slave pin is simply a short length of rod stock (in some cases, a section of a nail will do) which is used to keep two parts, or a part and a spring,

together during reassembly. The slave pin must be very slightly smaller in diameter than the hole in the part, so it will push out easily as the original pin is driven in to retain the part. When making a slave pin, its length should be slightly less than the width of the part in which it is being used, and the ends of the pin should be rounded or beveled.

Sights: Nearly all dovetail-mounted sights are drifted out toward the right, using a nylon, aluminum, or brass drift punch.

1. The tiniest of these fine German instrument screwdrivers from Brownells is too small for most gun work, but you'll see the rest of them used frequently throughout the book. There are many tight places where these will come in handy. Cost is about $17 for the set.

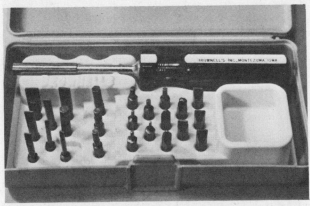

2. When a larger screwdriver is needed, this set from Brownells covers a wide range of blade sizes and also has Phillips- and Allen-type inserts. The tips are held in place by a strong magnet, yet are easily changed. These tips are very hard. With enough force you might manage to break one, but they'll never bend. Price of the complete set is about $21.

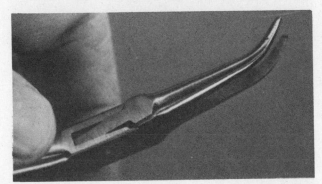

3. You should have at least one good pair of bent sharp-nosed pliers. These, from Brownells, have a box joint and smooth inner faces to help prevent marring. Price is about $8.

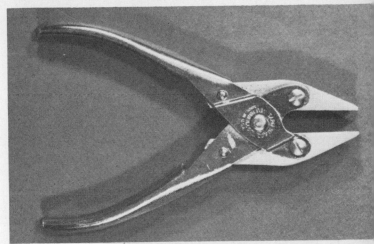

4. For heavier gripping, these Bernard parallel-jaw pliers from Brownells have smooth-faced jaw-pieces of unhardened steel to prevent marring of parts. Price is about $8.

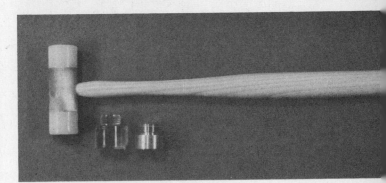

5. For situations where a non-marring rap is needed, this hammer from Brownells is ideal. It is shown with nylon faces on the head, but other faces of plastic and brass are also available. All are easily replaceable. Cost is about $8 with three faces.

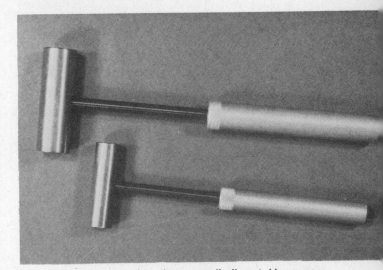

6. For drifting out pins, these small all-metal hammers from B-Square are the best I've seen. Two sizes (weights) are available and they're well worth the modest cost. About $15 for both.

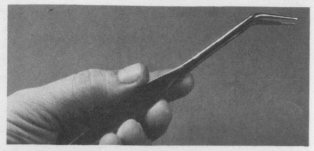

7. For situations where reach and accessability are beyond the capabilities of sharp-nosed pliers, a pair of large sharp-nosed forceps (tweezers) will be invaluable. From Brownells, about $2.

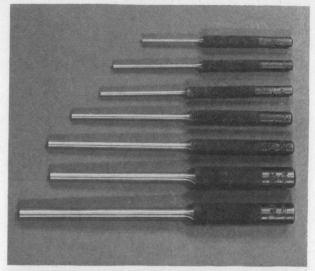

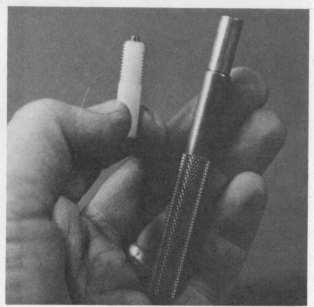

8. One of the most-used tools in my shop is this nylon-tipped drift punch, shown with an optional brass tip in place on the handle. It has a steel pin inside the nylon tip for strength. From Brownells, and absolutely essential. Price is about $2 for the set.

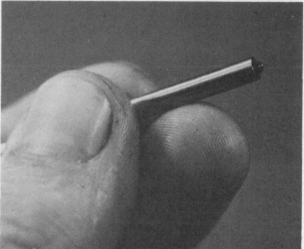

10. These punches by Mayhew are designed specifically for roll pins and have a projection at the center of the tip to fit the hollow center of a roll pin, driving it out without deformation of the ends. From Brownells, about $12 for the set.

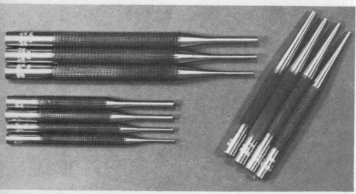

9. A good set of drift punches will prevent a lot of marred pins. These, from Brownells, are made by Mayhew. The tapered punches at the right are for starting pins, the others for pushing them through. Two sizes are available—4 inches (about 98¢ each) or 6 inches (about $1.25).

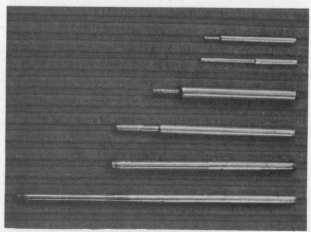

11. Some of the necessary tools are easily made in the shop. These non-marring drift punches were made from three sizes of welder's brazing rod.

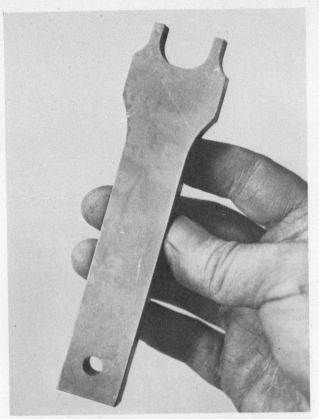

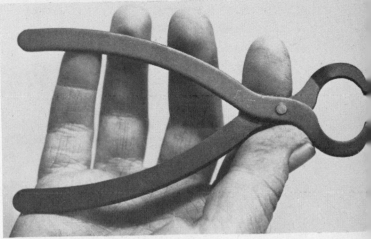

14. These extractor pliers are used in both the removal and replacement of Mauser or Springfield type extractors, making a difficult job much easier. From Brownells, $4.75.

12. This heavy wrench from Brownells is designed specifically for removal of the barrel nut in Remington Model 742 and Model 760 rifles. A quality tool of 01 steel, hardened to Rockwell C 46-48, it sells for $21.35.

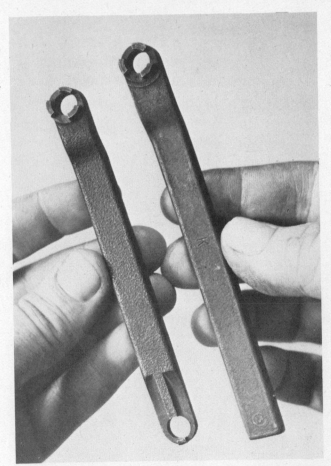

13. Most Remington centerfire rifles have the extractor mounted inside the front of the bolt by a tiny rivet, difficult to replace. This special tool from B-Square will set these rivets with a minimum of trouble. $31.95.

15. These wrenches are designed for removal of the piston nut in the 30 U.S. Carbine. The tool at the right is the original military type with three lugs, and the one at the left is a double-end type, to fit both the military guns and the two-slot nut found on some commercial civilian carbines. These wrenches are available from several military surplus and commercial sources.

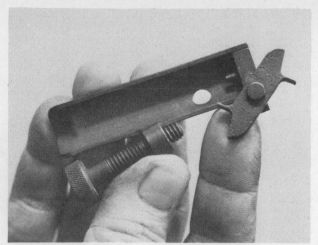

16. Without this tool, removal of the firing pin, ejector, and extractor from the 30 U.S. Carbine is a tedious job. It is available from military surplus sources.

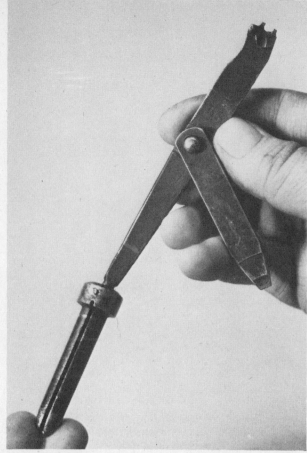

17. This combination tool for the U.S. M-1 rifle (Garand) has provisions for cleaning the chamber, installing the extractor and ejector in the bolt, a screwdriver, and other features. A completely-equipped Garand has one of these in the storage trap in the buttstock. They are available from military surplus sources.

BRITISH SMLE NO.1, MARK III

Data:	British SMLE No. 1 Mark III
Origin:	England
Manufacturer:	British Military Arsenals
Cartridge:	303 British
Magazine capacity:	10 rounds
Over-all length:	44½ inches
Barrel length:	25.19 inches
Weight:	8.62 pounds

In a bewildering array of "numbers" and "marks," the Lee-Enfield rifle was the mainstay of the British Military from 1895 to 1951. One version that is familiar to most U.S. shooters is the No. 1 Mark III rifle, as many of these were sold as surplus after World War II. For the benefit of those who came in late, "SMLE" is an abbreviation for "Short, Magazine, Lee-Enfield." Although the rifle was replaced in British service by the semi-auto L1A1 (FN FAL) in 1951, the old SMLE is still in use in many former British colonies and in other parts of the world.

Disassembly:

1. Remove the magazine. Open the bolt, and move it all the way to the rear. Lift the bolt head lug on the right side, disengaging it from the detent spring on the receiver, and turn it up to vertical position. Withdraw the bolt from the rear of the receiver. Some amount of pressure may be needed to turn the bolt head, but be sure that the bolt is fully to the rear before exerting force.

2. The bolt head is removed by simply unscrewing it from the front of the bolt, counter-clockwise (front view).

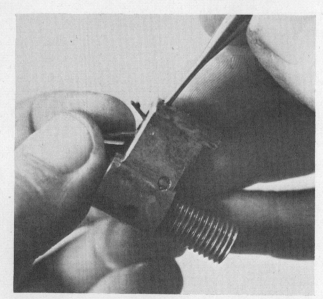

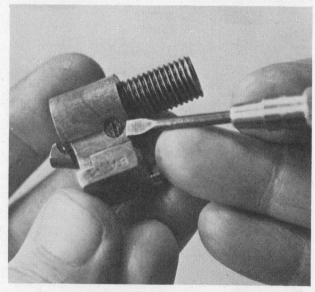

3. Insert a small-diameter tool in the hole in the outer surface of the bolt head lug, and push gently inward to disengage the extractor spring stud from its recess. The spring can then be pushed out toward the front. **Caution:** *The spring is under tension. Control it, and ease it out.*

4. The extractor is retained in the bolt head by a cross-screw. After the screw is taken out, the extractor is removed toward the front.

6. Removal of the striker/firing pin unit requires a special tool, easily made from brass or steel tubing having a ⅜-inch outside diameter. The working end of the tool is filed as shown in step 7, leaving twin projections which are designed to engage the recesses on the striker collar. The tool is inserted into the front of the bolt, and the striker unit is unscrewed from the knob at the rear. **Caution:** *Keep firm inward pressure during this operation, as the tension of the striker spring will be released when the threads are cleared.*

5. Remove the screw in the rear face of the cocking piece, at the rear of the bolt.

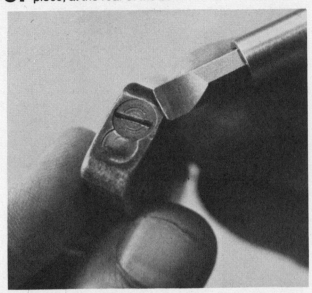

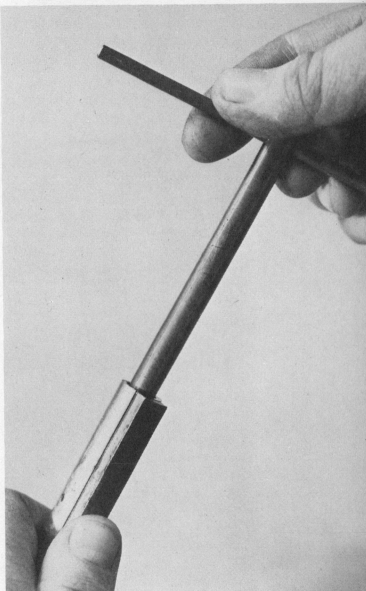

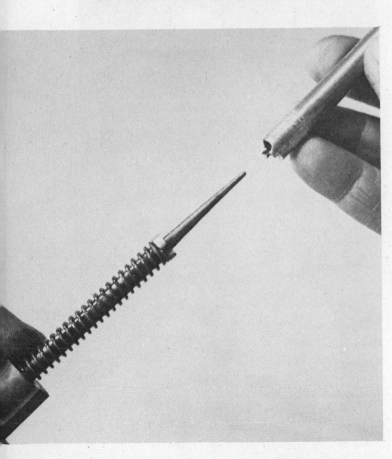

7. Remove the striker and its spring from the front of the bolt.

8. When the striker is released toward the front, the cocking knob will be freed at the rear, and will simply drop off.

9. Remove the cross-screw from the stock nose-cap. Remove the vertical screw on the underside of the stock nose-cap, located just to the rear of the bayonet mount. Then remove the stock nose-cap toward the front.

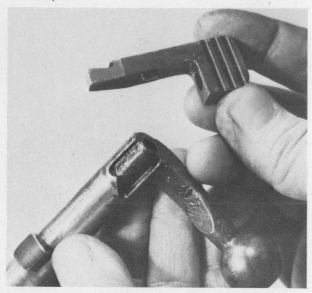

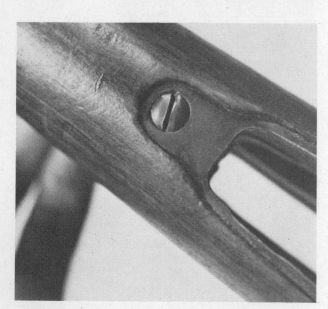

10. Remove the vertical screw on the underside of the stock, just forward of the magazine well.

11. Remove the cross-screw at the rear of the trigger guard, and take off the trigger guard unit downward and toward the rear.

12. Pushing out the cross-pin will release the trigger for removal upward.

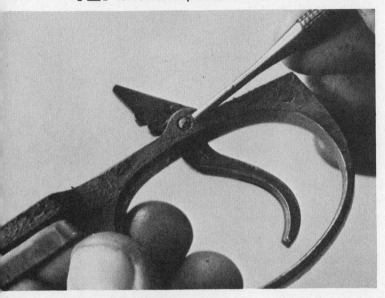

13. Remove the cross-screw in the rear stock/barrel band, releasing the sling loop, and spread the band (it is hinged at the top) for removal upward. This will allow the front handguard wood to be taken off toward the front and upward.

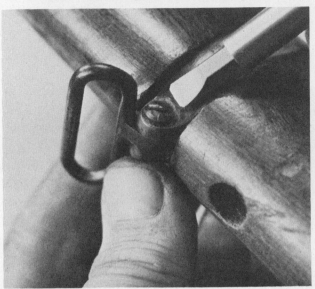

14. Remove the vertical screw on the underside of the stock, just to the rear of the rear band. The front lower section of the stock can now be moved forward and taken off.

15. Remove the fore-end stud and its spring from their well inside the stock, near the muzzle end.

16. The rear sight guard is retained in the stock by a vertical screw, and is removed upward.

17. If removal of the buttstock is necessary, you must first use a sharpened bent wire (such as an opened coathanger) to extract the leather washer that covers the head of the stock bolt. After this is removed, use a B-Square stock tool or a large screwdriver to back out the stock bolt, and take off the stock toward the rear. Enfield stock bolts are often rusted in place, and some effort may be required to effect removal.

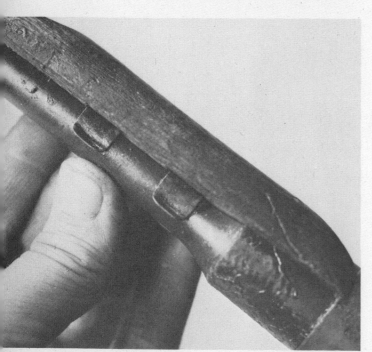

18. The rear upper handguard wood is retained on top of the barrel by twin spring-clips, and is snapped off upward the toward the rear. Raise the rear sight when taking off the handguard, and take care not to break the two slim front hand-guard projections.

19. Remove the screw on the right side of the receiver that retains the bolt head latch spring. This screw is also the pivot and retainer for the sear, and will release the sear and the combination sear and magazine catch spring for removal toward the rear and downward.

20. After the screw has been partially backed out, use pliers to slightly compress the spring, as shown, to ease removal of the screw.

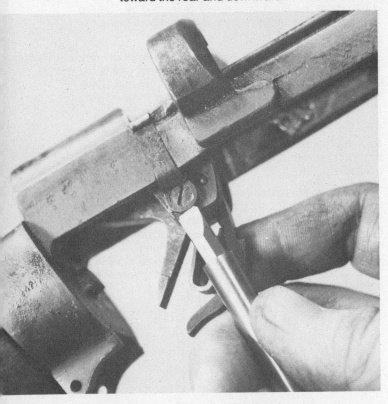

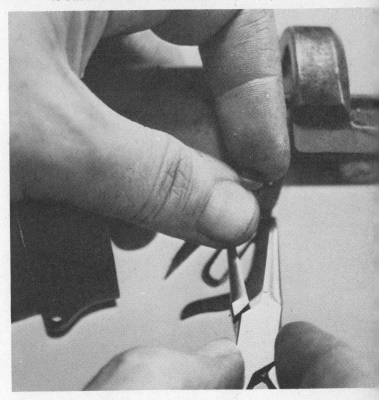

21. Drifting out the cross-pin will release the magazine catch for removal downward.

22. Pivoting the rear sight up to the vertical position will expose the mounting screw for the rear sight spring. After the spring is removed, the cross-pin can be drifted out to free the rear sight assembly. This pin is usually semi-riveted at each end, and is best left in place unless removal is necessary for repair.

23. Removal of the screw at the lower end of the safety spring on the left side will allow the spring to be taken off, and the safety lever and locking bolt can then be moved toward the left and taken out. The bolt lock piece is easily taken off the safety lever shaft by turning it around the shaft.

Reassembly Tips:

When replacing the trigger guard assembly, be sure the upper arm of the trigger is inserted *behind* the lower arm of the sear.

When replacing the safety system, turn the bolt lock on its fast helical threads until it is against the inner face of the lever, and hold it in this position while reinserting the assembly into the receiver, with the lever in its off-safe position.

When replacing the extractor spring in the bolt head, be sure the rear elbow of the spring enters the *outer* hole at the rear, and not the inner hole, where the extractor is pivoted.

When turning the striker shaft back into the cocking piece, be sure the rear tip of the shaft is level with the rear face of the cocking piece, as near as possible with proper alignment of the cut for the stop screw. This adjustment is critical, as it controls the protrusion of the firing pin point at the breech face. The protrusion should be no more than .055 inches and no less than .050 inches for proper primer contact.

BROWNING BAR

Data:	Browning BAR
Origin:	Belgium
Manufacturer:	Fabrique Nationale, Herstal, for Browning, Morgan, Utah
Cartridges:	243, 270, 30-06, 308, 7mm Remington Magnum, 300 Winchester Magnum
Magazine capacity:	4 rounds (3 in magnum)
Over-all length:	43 and 45 inches
Barrel length:	22 and 24 inches
Weight:	7⅜ and 8⅜ pounds

The factory designation of this gas-operated semiauto sporter has caused a little confusion, as the famed military selective-fire gun was also called the "BAR." The sleek sporting rifle was introduced in 1967, and it is still in production. The gun is offered in several grades, the price depending on the extent of stock checkering, carving, engraving, and inlay work. Regardless of the grade, the mechanical details are the same, and the instructions will apply.

Disassembly:

1. With the empty magazine in place, pull back the cocking handle to lock the bolt in open position. With a small wrench or a pair of smooth-jawed pliers, unscrew the front sling swivel base, on the underside of the fore-end near the forward end.

2. Tip the front of the fore-end downward until firm resistance is felt, then move it forward and off. Do this carefully, and use no extreme force, or the fore-end will be damaged.

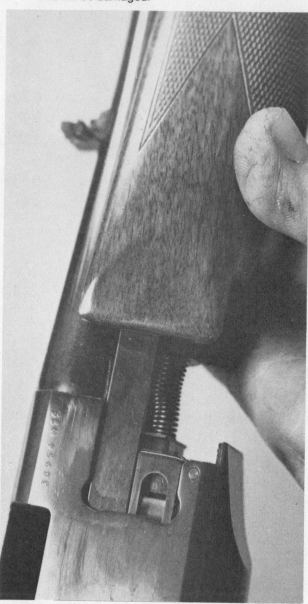

3. Slide the right and left action rod support rails out of the receiver toward the front, and remove them.

4. Disengage the forward ends of the action bars from the studs on the sides of the intertia block, and take the bars out toward the front.

5. Remove the gas regulator from the front end of the gas cylinder. A ⅝-inch open-end wrench will fit the side flats of the regulator, and it is simply unscrewed. Be sure the wrench is properly engaged to prevent marring. Take care not to lose the lock washer behind the gas regulator.

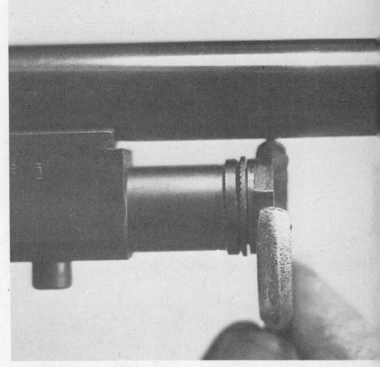

6. Remove the gas piston toward the front. If the piston is very tight, it may have to be nudged from the rear with a drift punch. If this is necessary, be very careful, as any burrs raised will cause the system to malfunction. If the piston won't move with the use of reasonable force, soak it for a time in a good powder solvent or penetrant.

7. Firmly grip the action spring guide at the rear, and lift its rear tip out of its seat in the front of the receiver. Remove the guide, spring, and inertia block toward the rear. **Caution:** *Keep a firm grip on the partially compressed spring, and ease it off.*

8. Open the magazine floorplate, and insert a small screwdriver at the rear of the magazine to pry it away from the floorplate. Remove the magazine from the floorplate.

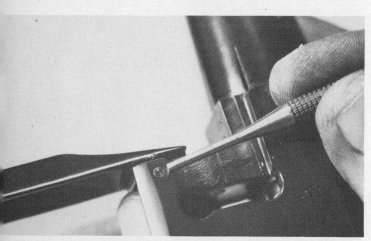

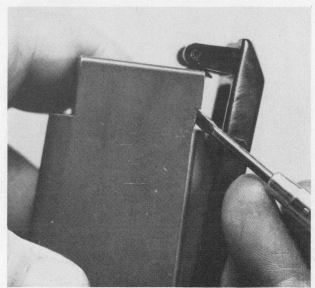

9. The magazine retaining spring is mounted on the end of the floorplate by a cross-pin, and is easily removed. The floorplate is attached to the receiver by a cross-pin, and the floorplate spring is mounted around the pin. Restrain the spring when drifting out the cross-pin, and remove the floorplate downward.

10. Remove the buttplate to give access to the stock mounting bolt. Use a B-Square stock tool or a long screwdriver to remove the stock mounting bolt, and take off the stock toward the rear. If it is very tight, bump the front of the comb with the heel of the hand to start it.

11. Insert a drift punch into the hole in the stock mounting plate at the rear of the receiver, and lift the plate upward, then tip it and remove it toward the rear.

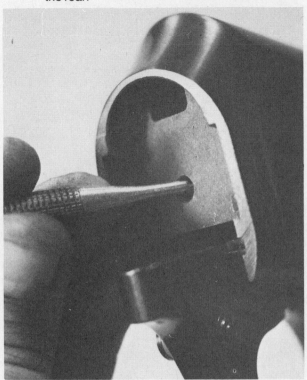

12. Slide the trigger group out of the receiver toward the rear.

13. Restrain the hammer, pull the trigger, and ease the hammer down to the fired position. Drift out the trigger cross-pin.

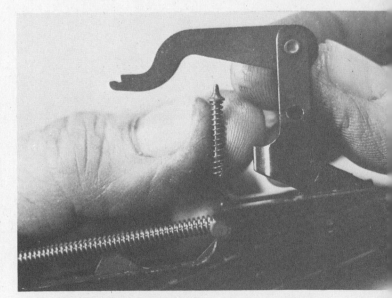

14. Remove the trigger and the attached disconnector upward, and take out the disconnector spring and its plunger. The cross-pin that joins the disconnector to the trigger is riveted in place, and should be removed only for repair or replacement purposes.

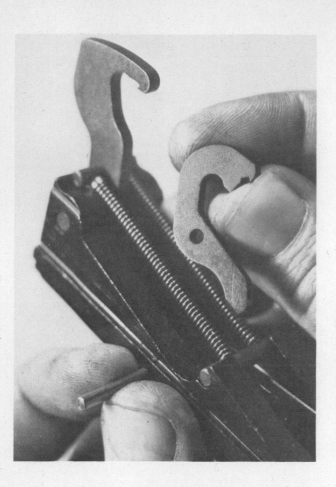

15. Push out the sear cross-pin, move the sear forward, then remove it upward.

16. Insert a screwdriver behind the base for the twin hammer springs and lever it forward and upward, out of its seats in the trigger group. **Caution:** *Grip the ends of the base firmly during this operation, and control its movement, as the semi-compressed double springs are quite strong.* Remove the spring base, springs, guide rods, and the front base in the hammer.

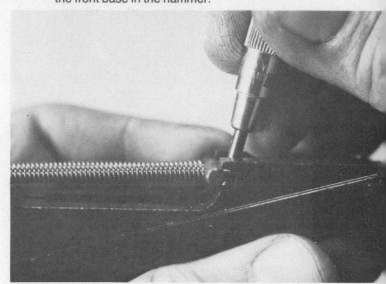

18. The magazine floorplate latch is retained in the receiver by a vertical roll pin, and this pin need not be drifted completely out to free the latch and spring. Just drift it upward enough to clear the latch, and take out the latch and spring toward the front.

17. Push out the hammer cross-pin, and take out the hammer upward.

19. A roll cross-pin at the rear of the trigger group retains the safety plunger and spring. Restrain the spring at the top when drifting out the pin, and remove the spring and plunger upward. Remove the safety toward either side.

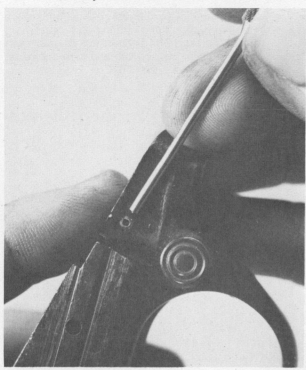

20. Move the bolt so the operating handle is accessible in the ejection port, and insert a small screwdriver to lift the handle latch outward. Move the handle forward, out of its recess in the bolt.

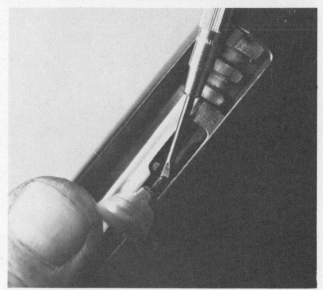

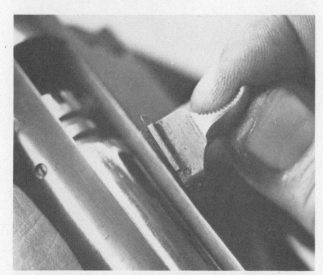

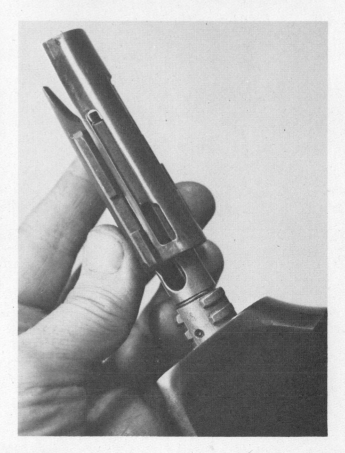

21. Move the operating handle to the wider opening in the bolt cover, and remove the handle toward the right. The latch and spring are retained in the handle by a very small cross-pin, and are easily removed. In normal takedown, they are best left in place.

22. After the handle is removed, move the bolt assembly about half-way to the rear, bring it downward from the roof of the receiver, and take it out toward the rear.

23. Move the bolt cover to the rear of the bolt, and push upward on the right lower edge, tipping it over toward the left, and snapping its guide flange out of the groove on the bolt.

24. Drift out the cross-pin in the rear tail of the bolt, and take out the firing pin and its return spring toward the rear. The ends of the cross-pin are contoured with the bolt tail, and care should be taken not to deform the ends.

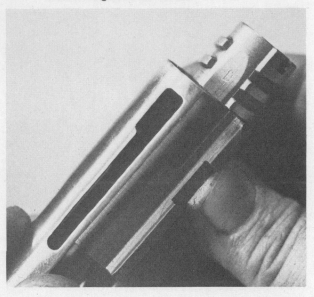

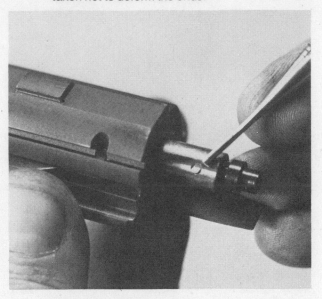

25. Push the cam pin upward out of the bolt sleeve, and remove it.

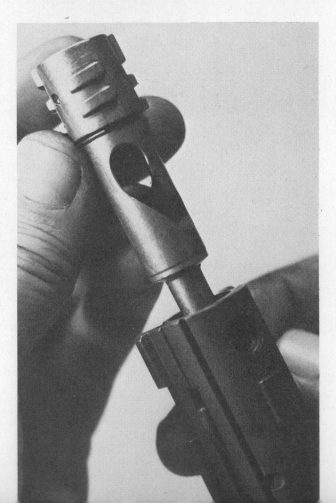

26. Move the bolt forward out of the bolt sleeve.

27. Drifting out the vertical pin on the left side of the bolt carrier will allow removal of the timing latch toward the left. The pin must be removed upward.

28. The ejector is retained at the front of the bolt by a vertical pin. **Caution:** *Restrain the ejector, and ease it out after removal of the pin, as the ejector spring is compressed.*

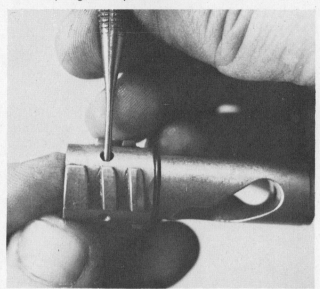

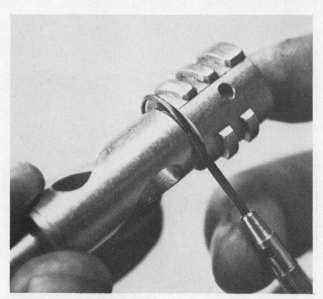

29. Use a small screwdriver to push the extractor spring up out of its groove, and remove the spring toward the rear.

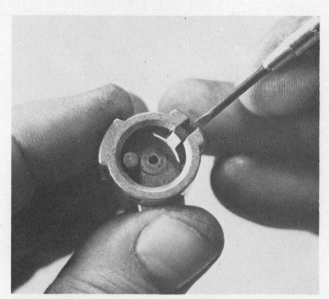

30. After the spring is removed, the extractor can be moved downward, into the bolt face recess, and is taken out toward the front.

Reassembly Tips:

1. When replacing the bolt in the bolt carrier, be sure the flat between the bolt lugs is on *top,* and the extractor and ejector at upper left and lower right (front view).

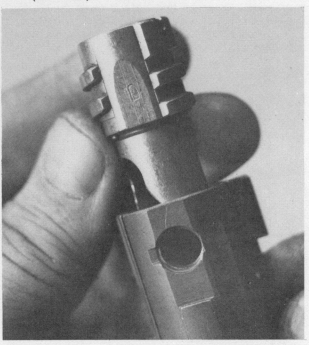

2. When replacing the cam pin in the bolt and sleeve, the small hole at the center of the cam pin must be oriented properly for passage of the firing pin.

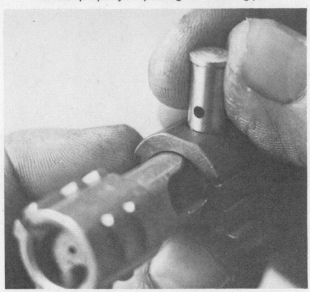

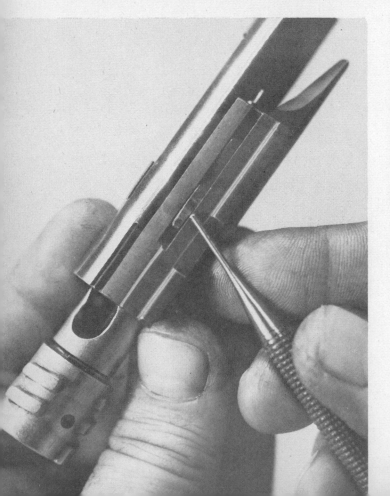

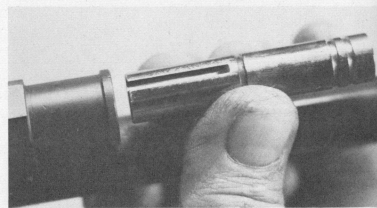

4. When replacing the gas piston, note that there is a guide pin at the lower rear of the gas cylinder, and the piston must be oriented so its rear groove will mate with the pin.

3. When replacing the bolt in the receiver, the bolt must be at its forward position in the sleeve, to allow the timing latch to be retracted.

JAPANESE ARISAKA TYPE 99

Data: Japanese Arisaka Type 99
Origin: Japan
Manufacturer: Tokyo Arsenal, Nagoya Arsenal
Cartridge: 7.7mm Japanese
Magazine capacity: 5 rounds
Over-all length: 50 inches (short version, 43.9 inches)
Barrel length: 31.4 inches (short version, 25.8 inches)
Weight: 9.1 pounds (short version, 8.6 pounds)

Although the early Type 38 rifle is occasionally seen in the U.S., the one most familiar to American shooters and collectors is the Type 99, adopted in 1939. The Type 99 is a modified Mauser design, and is one of the strongest actions ever made. Late wartime guns, though, are often of dubious quality in both materials and fitting. Early well-made guns were once popular for conversion into sporting rifles. There are several small mechanical differences between the Type 38 and Type 99 rifles, especially in the bolt stop/ejector system.

Disassembly:

1. To remove the bolt, open it and move it to the rear. Pivot the bolt stop out toward the left, and withdraw the bolt from the rear of the receiver.

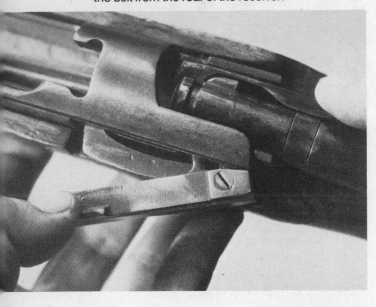

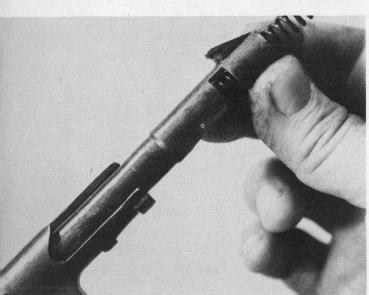

3. Remove the striker and its internal spring toward the rear.

4. Rotate the extractor on its collar until its front underlug is out of its groove, and push it off toward the front, disengaging its T-slot from the mounting flanges on the ring. Removal of the ring from the bolt is not advisable in normal takedown.

2. To remove the combination safety and bolt end-piece, grip the bolt firmly, and push the safety knob toward the front until it stops. Then, turn it counter-clockwise (rear view) until it stops, and let it move toward the rear, slowly easing the tension of the striker spring. Remove the safety knob toward the rear.

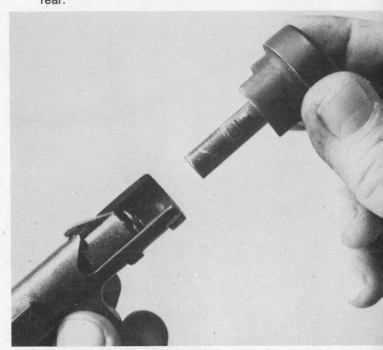

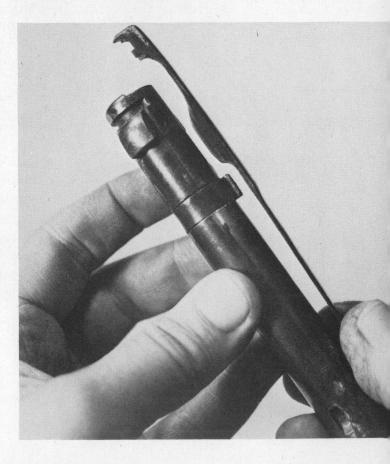

5. Remove the large cross-screw in the front barrel band, and the two side screws in the rear tabs of the band. Slide the band forward off the front of the stock.

6. Remove the cross-screw in the rear barrel band, and slide it forward off the stock. Move the upper hand-guard wood forward, then lift it off the top of the barrel.

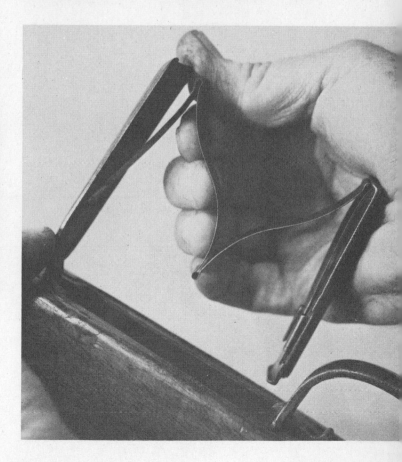

7. Operate the magazine floorplate latch to release the floorplate, and slide the magazine spring out of its recess in the floorplate. The follower can be taken off the top of the spring in the same way. Re-close the floorplate.

8. Remove the three vertical screws on the underside, located in front of the magazine floorplate, behind the trigger guard, and at the end of the lower tang.

9. Remove the trigger guard/magazine housing unit downward, and take off the action upward. The upper tang piece can also be lifted out upward, separately.

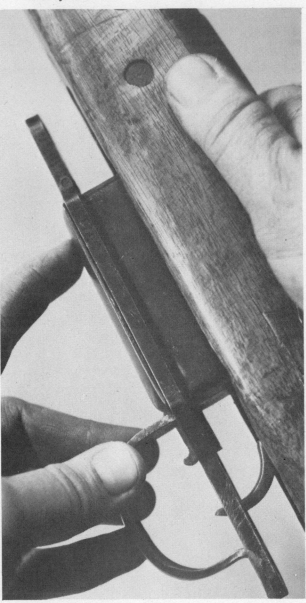

10. Removal of the barrel bands from the barrel requires that the front sight be taken off, and this is not advisable in normal takedown.

11. The rear sight can be removed from its base by drifting out the cross-pin at the rear of the sight, but the base is not removable in normal takedown.

12. To remove the bolt stop/ejector assembly, take out the vertical screw at its rear, and remove the assembly toward the left.

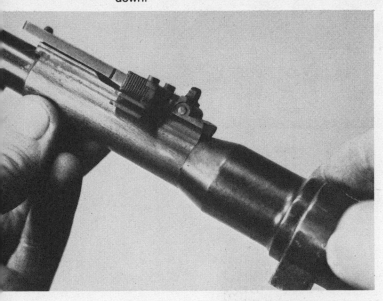

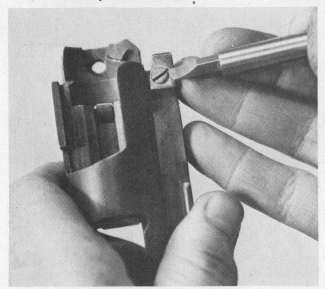

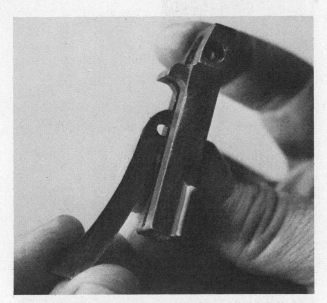

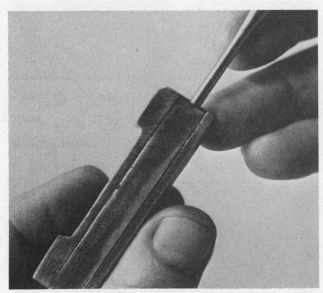

13. The ejector can be pulled out of the bolt stop toward the front.

14. To remove the combination bolt stop and ejector spring, place a small drift punch against its rear edge and use a small hammer to tap it toward the front. When the rear tip of the spring has cleared the cross-piece at the rear of the bolt stop it will drop inside. If necessary, insert a small screwdriver to lever it forward until it can be grasped at the front and taken out.

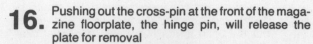

15. The magazine box is a press fit in the guard unit, and is easily worked loose and lifted out.

16. Pushing out the cross-pin at the front of the magazine floorplate, the hinge pin, will release the plate for removal

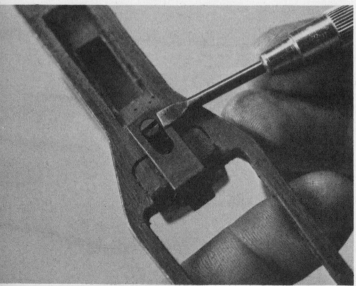

17. A vertical screw on the inside of the guard unit retains the magazine floorplate latch and its spring. After the screw is taken out, the latch and spring are removed toward the front.

18. The trigger/sear assembly is retained on the underside of the receiver by a cross-pin. Exerting pressure on the front of the sear to slightly compress the spring will make removal of the pin easier. The sear, trigger, and spring are removed downward.

19. Drifting out the cross-pin at the top of the trigger will allow separation of the sear and trigger.

Reassembly Tips:

1. After the combination bolt stop and ejector spring is inserted in the bolt stop, its rear tip will stop against the rear cross-bar of the stop. Insert a small drift punch or screwdriver through the upper hole in the bolt stop, to bear against the inner shelf of the spring tip, lifting it onto the bar and levering it toward the rear. The spring can then be tapped into place from the front.

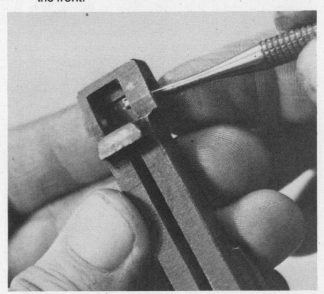

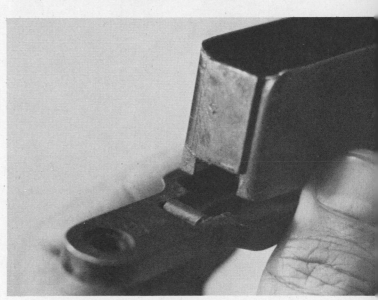

2. When replacing the magazine housing in its recess on top of the guard unit, note that the rectangular cut at the front goes at the bottom, next to the unit, to give clearance for the floorplate hinge.

3. When replacing the extractor on the bolt, turn the mounting ring so its upper projections are aligned with the oblong vent hole in the bolt. This will bring the un-grooved area at the front of the bolt in line for re-attachment of the extractor. As the extractor is slid back onto the mounting ring, its front underlug will be stopped by the front edge of the bolt, and it must be lifted slightly at the front to clear. After the extractor is fully to the rear, turn it back until the front underlug enters the retaining groove.

4. When replacing the striker and its spring in the bolt, be sure the underlug of the striker is in the cocked detent, as shown, to allow replacement of the safety knob.

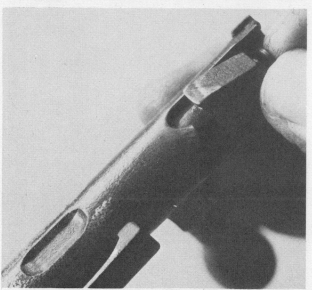

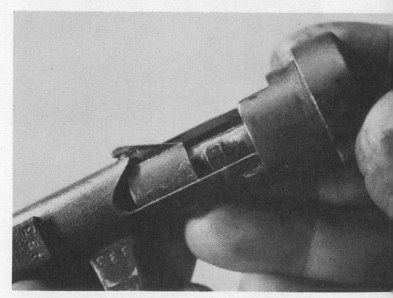

5. When replacing the safety knob, it must be aligned so the lug on its front shaft will enter the inside track on the striker, as shown.

MARLIN MODEL 336

Data:	Marlin Model 336
Origin:	United States
Manufacturer:	Marlin Firearms Company
	North Haven, Connecticut
Cartridge:	30-30 Winchester, 35 Remington
Magazine capacity:	6 rounds
Over-all length:	38½ inches
Barrel length:	20 inches
Weight:	7 pounds

An extensive re-design of the Marlin Model 36 (1936) rifle, the Model 336 was first offered in 1948. It was initially available in several calibers, but in recent years only the 30-30 and 35 chamberings have been in production. Although most lever action guns are generally more complicated than other manually-operated actions, the Model 336 has a relatively easy takedown, with no really difficult points. Several sub-models of this gun were made, and the instructions will apply to any of these.

Disassembly:

1. Partially open the lever, and take out the lever pivot cross-screw. Remove the lever downward.

2. Remove the bolt toward the rear.

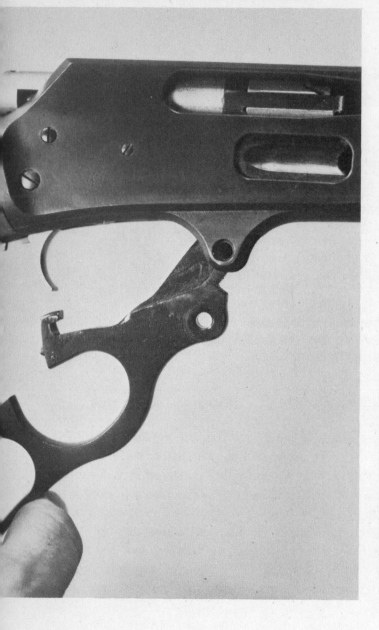

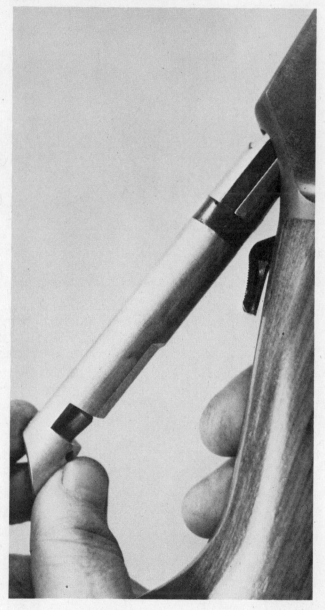

3. Push the ejector mounting stud inward, and remove the ejector from inside the receiver. The ejector spring is staked in place, and removal in normal disassembly is not advisable, except for repair.

4. Drifting out the vertical roll pin at the rear of the bolt will release the rear firing pin and its spring for removal toward the rear.

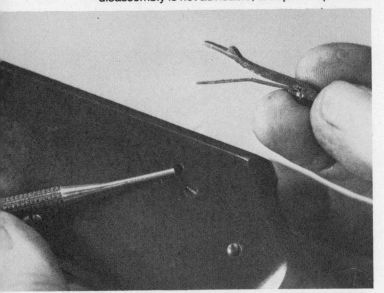

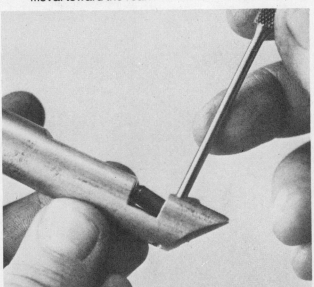

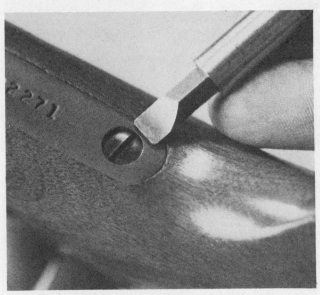

5. Use a small screwdriver to pry the extractor clip off its recess on the front of the bolt, using a finger-tip to lift the front of the extractor out of its channel. Removal of the extractor will give access to the vertical pin that retains the front firing pin. After the pin is drifted out, the firing pin is removed toward the rear.

6. Remove the vertical screw at the rear of the upper tang, and take off the stock toward the rear. If the stock is tight, bump the front of the comb with the heel of the hand to start it off.

7. Depress the trigger block (arrow), on the underside behind the trigger, and gently lower the hammer to the fired position. With smooth-jawed pliers or strong fingers, grip the upper portion of the hammer spring base plate, tilt it forward, and slide it toward the side, moving its lower end out of its groove in the lower tang. Keep a firm grip on the plate, as the spring is under some tension, even when at rest. Remove the plate, and the hammer spring, toward the rear.

8. Remove the hammer pivot screw, and take out the hammer upward. Drifting out the cross-pin at the rear of the hammer will release the hammer spring strut, but in normal takedown it is best left in place.

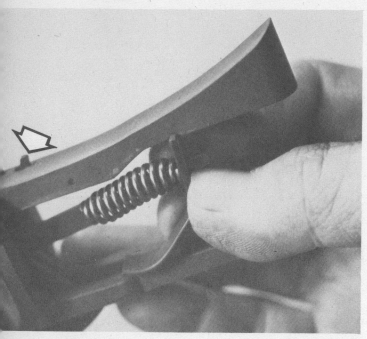

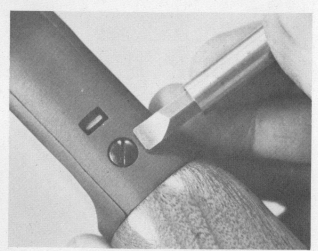

9. Remove the vertical screw on the underside at the forward end of the trigger housing.

10. Remove the screw on the left side of the receiver at lower center.

11. Remove the trigger housing downward and toward the rear. If it is very tight, it may be necessary to tap it with a plastic hammer to start it out.

12. Drifting out the trigger cross-pin will allow the trigger and sear to be removed downward. The small pin just forward of the trigger is the contact for the lever latch, and does not have to be removed.

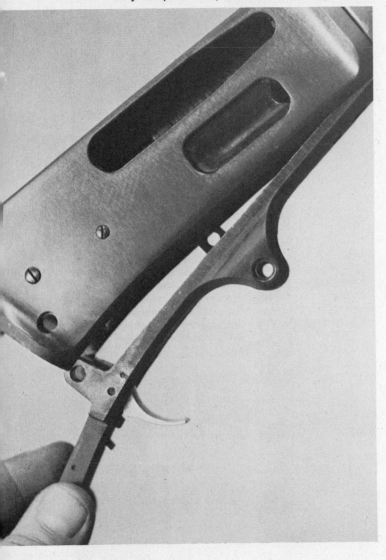

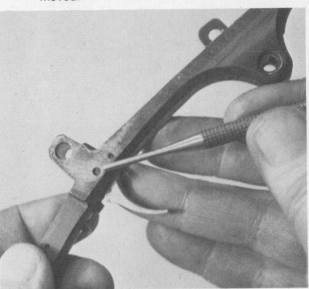

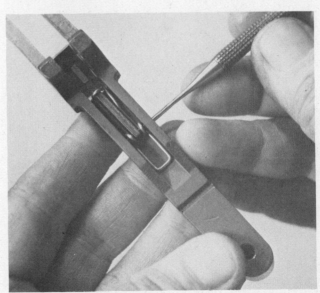

13. A small cross-pin in the lower tang portion of the trigger housing retains the trigger safety block and the combination spring that powers the block and the trigger/sear system. After the pin is drifted out, the block and spring are removed upward. **Note:** The spring is under tension. Control it, and ease it out.

14. The lever latch plunger and its spring are retained in the lever by a cross-pin, and are removed toward the rear. The short coil spring is quite strong, so control it and ease it out.

15. After the trigger housing plate is taken off, the bolt locking block can be moved downward out of the receiver.

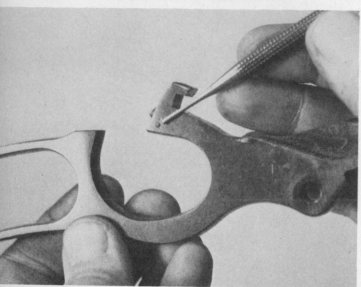

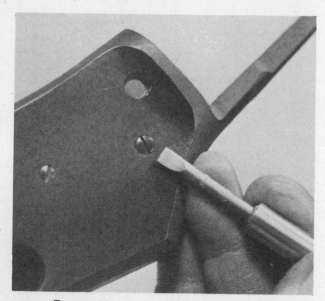

16. Remove the carrier pivot screw, located on the right side of the receiver at center rear.

17. Remove the carrier downward. The carrier rocker and its spring are retained on the left side of the carrier by a vertical pin.

18. Remove the small screw on the right side of the receiver to the rear of the loading port, and take out the loading gate from inside the receiver.

19. Remove the screw on the underside of the magazine tube at its forward end, and take out the tube endpiece, magazine spring, and follower. **Caution:** *Some magazine springs are more powerful than others, and all are under some tension. Ease the endpiece out, and control the spring.*

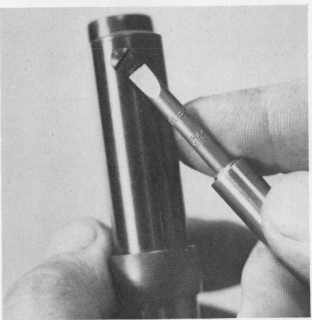

20. Slide the front sight hood off toward the front, remove the two vertical screws in the front sight base, and take off the front sight upward.

21. Take out the cross-screw in the front barrel band. Take out the cross-screw in the rear barrel band, and slide the barrel band off toward the front.

22. Move the fore-end wood forward to free the magazine tube, then slide the magazine tube, fore-end wood, and front barrel band off toward the front.

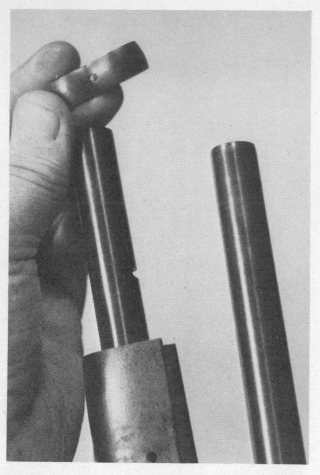

Reassembly Tips:

1. When replacing the magazine tube, be sure its rear tip enters the well in the front of the receiver. Be sure it is oriented at the front so its screw groove will align with the hole in the front barrel band.

2. When replacing the hammer spring system, hook the lower end of the spring plate in its groove in the lower tang, tip the top of the plate forward, beneath the upper tang, and slide the plate across into place.

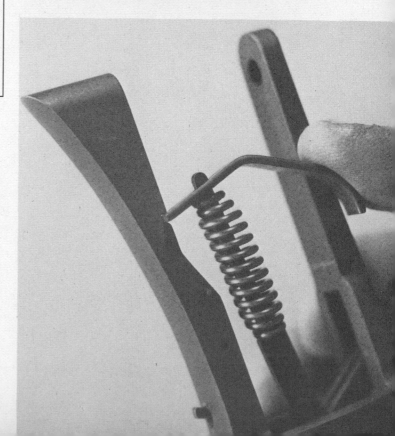

MAUSER MODEL 1898

Data: Mauser Model 1898 (Karabiner 98k)
Origin: Germany
Manufacturer: Various government arsenals
Cartridge: 7.92mm Mauser (8×57mm Mauser)
Magazine capacity: 5 rounds
Over-all length: 43.6 inches
Barrel length: 23.62 inches
Weight: 9 pounds

The classic Model 1898 Mauser rifle was made in both military and sporting versions from 1898 to 1935, when the military rifle was redesigned to become the Model 98k, the famous Karabiner of World War II. After the war, countless numbers of 98k guns were brought into the U.S. as war souvenirs, and later a large quantity of stored guns were sold on the surplus market. The actions were popular as the basis for sporting rifles, while the full military guns in top condition were a prize for collectors. Many of today's finest commercial sporting rifles have action designs based on the original Mauser 98 system.

Disassembly:

1. Cycle the bolt to cock the striker, and turn the safety lever up to the vertical position. Open the bolt, and move it toward the rear while holding the bolt stop pulled out toward the left. Remove the bolt from the rear of the receiver.

2. Depress the bolt sleeve lock plunger, located on the left side, and unscrew the bolt sleeve counter-clockwise (rear view), taking care not to trip the safety lever from its vertical position. Remove the bolt sleeve and striker assembly toward the rear.

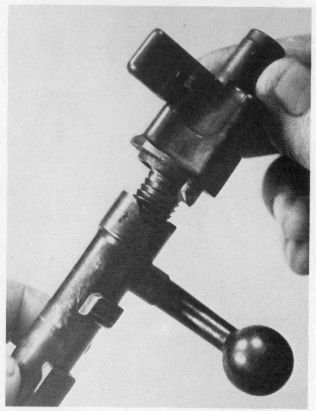

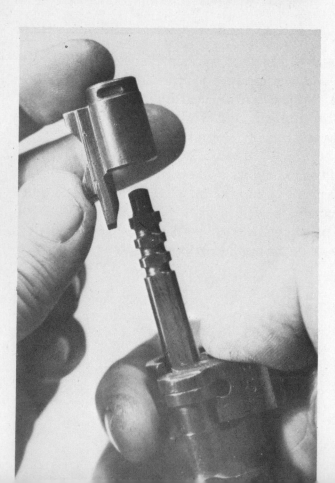

3. If the round takedown bushing is still in the side of the buttstock, insert the firing pin section of the striker shaft into the hole in the center of the bushing to hold the assembly for takedown. If the gun does not have the original stock and bushing, grip the front of the striker in a vise. Either way, take care to exert no side pressure. Holding the bolt sleeve against the tension of the striker spring, turn the safety lever back to off-safe position, and push the bolt sleeve toward the front until the rear edge of the sleeve clears the front of the cocking piece underlug. Turn the cocking piece a quarter-turn in either direction, and remove it from the rear end of the striker shaft. **Caution:** *Keep a firm grip on the bolt sleeve, holding the compressed striker spring.*

4. Slowly release the spring tension, moving the bolt sleeve off the rear of the striker shaft, and removing the spring toward the rear.

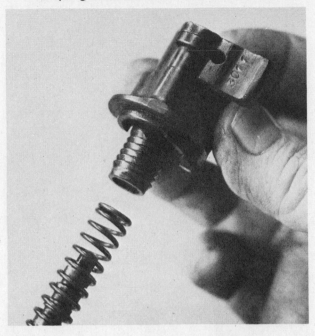

5. Turn the safety lever over to the right side (clockwise, rear view), and remove it toward the rear.

6. To remove the bolt sleeve lock plunger and its spring, push the plunger inward, and turn it to bring its retaining stud into the exit track. Remove the plunger and spring toward the front.

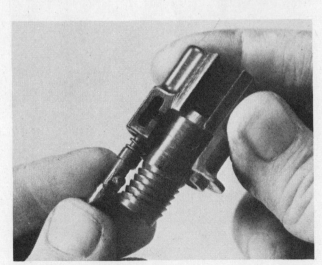

7. If you have the Brownells extractor pliers, use them to raise the front of the extractor just enough to clear the groove at the front of the bolt. A screwdriver inserted beneath the extractor can also do this. With the extractor lifted, turn it clockwise (rear view) until it is aligned with the grooveless area at the front of the bolt.

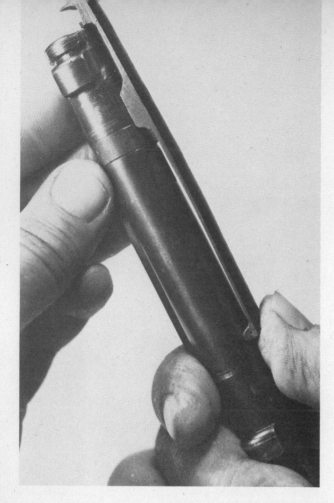

8. Push the extractor straight off toward the front. The mounting ring is not removed from the bolt in normal disassembly.

9. Insert a medium-sized drift punch in the hole at the rear of the magazine floorplate, and depress the floorplate latch. Move the floorplate toward the rear.

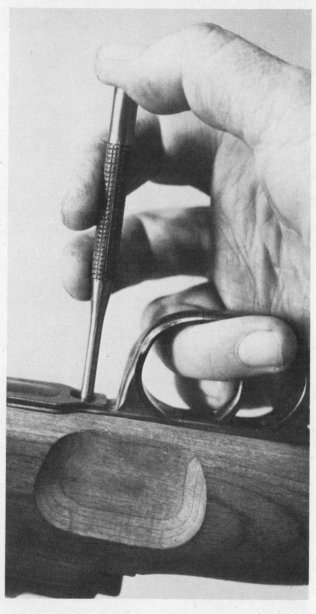

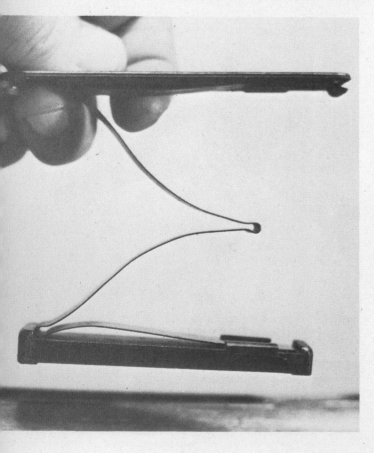

10. Remove the magazine floorplate, spring, and follower downward. The spring is easily detached from the plate and follower.

11. If the end section of cleaning rod is present in the front of the stock, unscrew it and remove it. Depress the front barrel band latch and slide the barrel band off toward the front.

12. The spring latch is now free to be removed from its recess in the stock, and the rear barrel band can be slid off forward and removed. The upper handguard wood can also be taken off at this time.

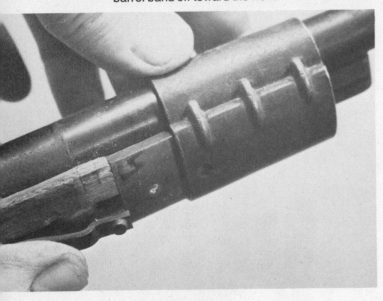

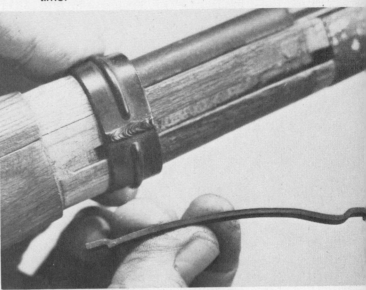

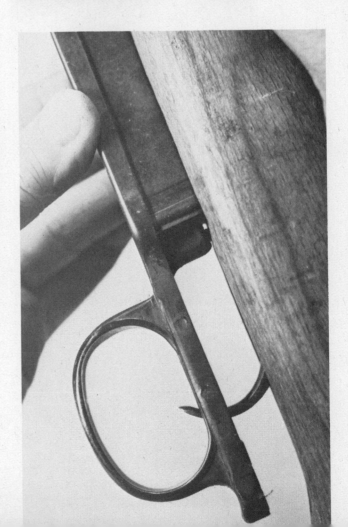

13. Remove the lock screws, and take out the larger vertical screws on the underside of the stock at the front and rear of the trigger/magazine housing.

14. Remove the trigger/magazine housing downward, and separate the action from the stock.

15. The magazine floorplate latch is retained by a cross-pin in the trigger/magazine housing, and is removed downward. **Caution:** *This is a very strong spring, so control the plunger and ease it out.*

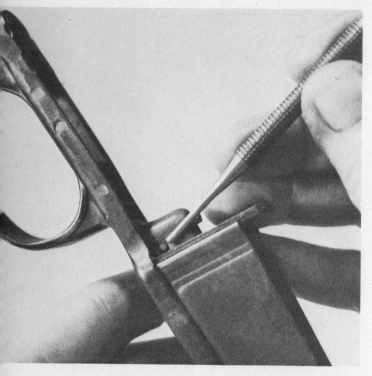

16. Remove the small vertical screw at the left rear of the receiver, the pivot for the bolt stop. Then remove the bolt latch/ejector assembly toward the left side.

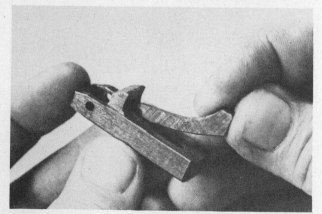

17. Remove the ejector toward the front.

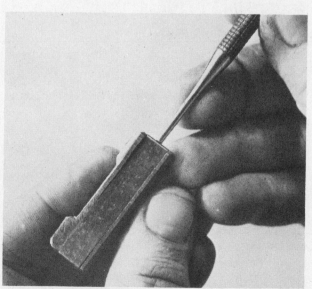

18. To remove the combination bolt latch and ejector spring, set a drift punch against its rear edge, and drive it out toward the front. When the rear tip has cleared the cross-piece at the rear of the bolt latch, the tip of the spring will move inward, and can then be levered out toward the front with a screwdriver blade.

Reassembly Tips:

19. Drifting out the cross-pin that retains the sear will allow removal of the sear, sear spring, and the attached trigger downward. The trigger cross-pin can be drifted out to separate the trigger from the sear.

1. When replacing the combination bolt stop and ejector spring, it will be necessary to insert a screwdriver or some other tool to lift its rear tip onto the cross-piece at the rear of the bolt stop, as the spring is driven into place.

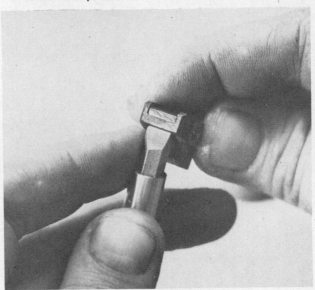

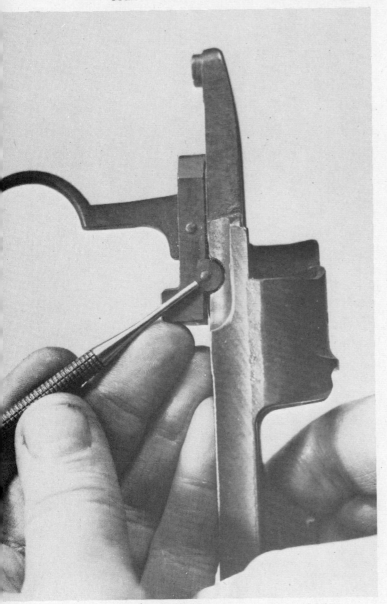

2. When replacing the extractor on the bolt, be sure the mounting ring flanges are aligned with the ungrooved area at the front of the bolt. Use the Brownells pliers or some other tool to compress the ring flanges, and slide the extractor onto the ring.

3. With the extractor pliers or a screwdriver blade, lift the front of the extractor while depressing the center of its tail, to lift the underlug at the front over the edge of the bolt face. When the underlug is aligned with the groove, turn the extractor back toward the left (counter-clockwise, rear view), until it covers the right lug of the bolt.

4. Before the bolt sleeve and striker assembly can be put back into the bolt, the striker must be moved to the rear and the safety turned into the vertical on-safe position. As the assembly is turned into place, the sleeve latch plunger must be pushed in twice— once to clear the bolt handle, and again as it enters its locking notch.

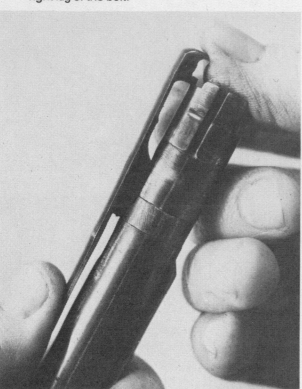
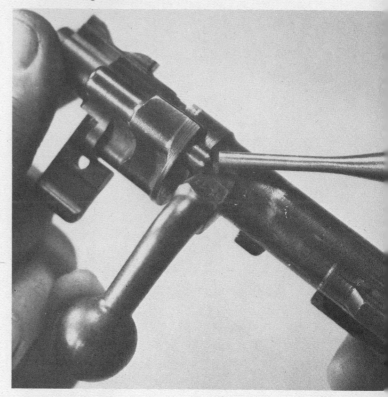

MOSIN-NAGANT

Data:	Russian Mosin-Nagant
Origin:	Russia
Manufacturers:	Russian arsenals in later years, earlier by contract in France, Switzerland, and by Remington and Westinghouse in America
Cartridge:	7.62mm Russian
Magazine capacity:	5 rounds
Over-all length:	51.3 inches (carbine, 40 inches)
Barrel length:	31.6 inches (carbine, 20 inches)
Weight:	9.63 pounds (carbine, 7.5 pounds)

The Russin Model 1891 rifle was designed by Colonel Sergei Ivanovitch Mosin, then chief of the Imperial Arsenal at Tula. The magazine system was designed by Emile Nagant of Belgium, thus giving the gun its popular name, Mosin-Nagant. This rifle was used by the Russian military forces from 1891 through World War II. Late-manufacture guns are often rather crude, but the design is simple and the operation reliable. The gun shown in the photos has been "sporterized," but the mechanical details are unchanged.

Disassembly:

1. Open the bolt, hold the trigger pulled to the rear, and remove the bolt from the rear of the receiver.

2. Grip the front of the bolt firmly, pull back the cocking knob, and turn it counter-clockwise (rear view) allowing the striker to move forward to the fired position.

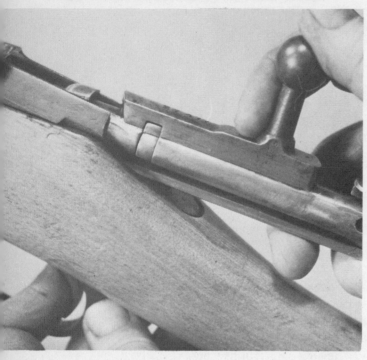

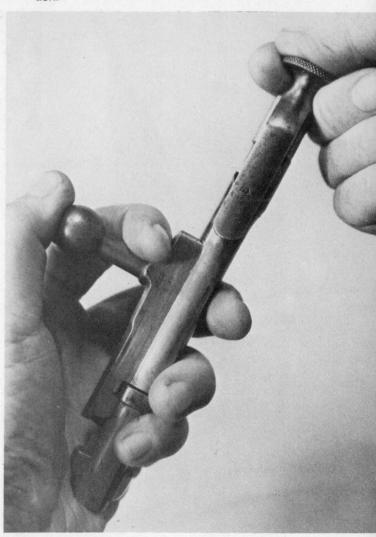

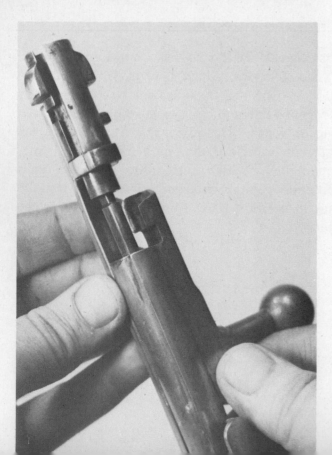

3. Slide the bolt connector and bolt head off toward the front.

4. Turn the bolt head counter-clockwise (rear view) until it stops and remove it from the bolt connector toward the front.

5. The extractor is dovetail-mounted in the bolt head, and should not be routinely removed. If necessary for repair, it is drifted out toward the rear. An un-broken extractor should be left in place.

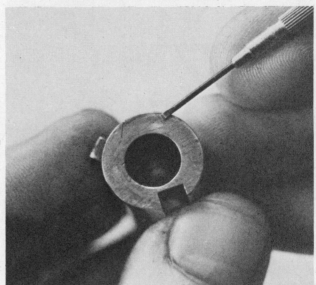

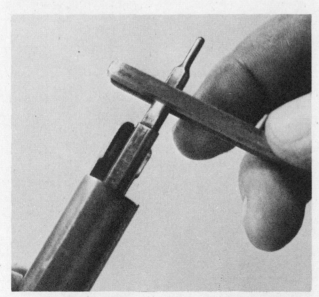

6. The striker is threaded into the cocking piece at the rear, and the rear forked tip of the bolt connector guide bar can be used as a wrench on the flat sides of the firing pin to unscrew it. If the striker is very tight, though, use a small wrench or smooth parallel-jawed pliers, as extreme force could break the tip of the bar. **Caution:** *Control the parts, as the striker spring will be released when the threads are cleared.*

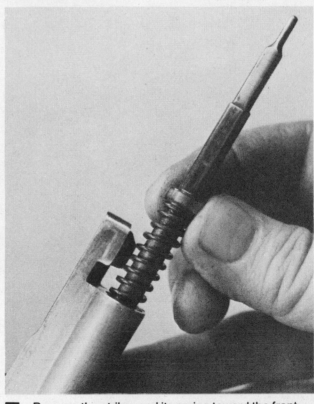

7. Remove the striker and its spring toward the front.

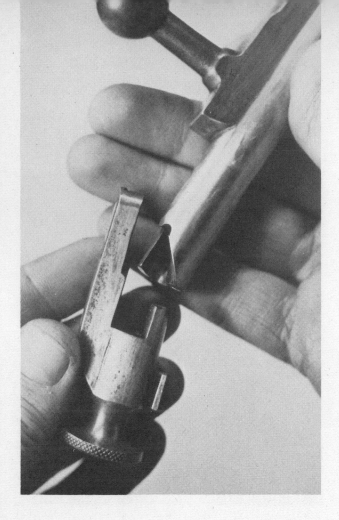

8. The cocking piece will be released at the rear of the bolt as the striker is unscrewed from the front.

9. With a fingertip or tool, push the magazine floorplate latch toward the rear, and open the floorplate.

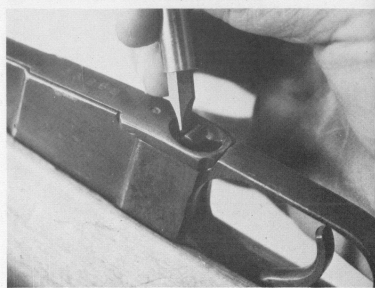

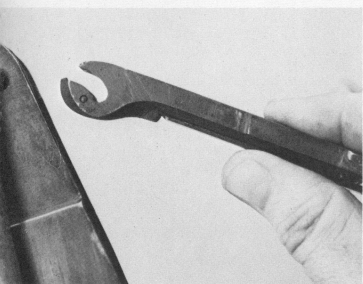

10. Squeeze the magazine follower down to the floorplate, and remove the floorplate assembly downward.

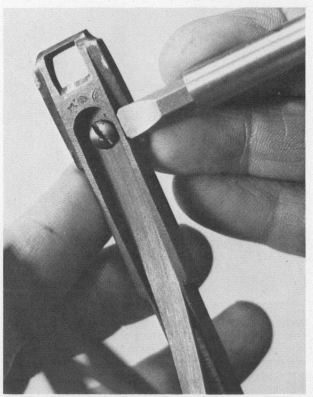

11. The magazine mainspring is retained inside the floorplate by a single screw.

12. After the screw and spring are removed, drifting out the cross-pin that pivots the follower arm will allow separation of the arm assembly from the floorplate.

13. The follower is also cross-pinned to the arm, and the follower spring is easily detached by depressing its upper end from the underside of the follower and swinging the spring toward the side.

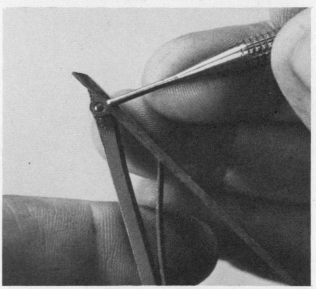

14. If the rifle still has the full military stock, there will be two barrel bands, retained by spring catches on the right side of the stock. Slide the bands off forward, and remove the upper handguard. Next, remove the vertical screw on top, at the rear edge of the bolt track.

15. Remove the vertical screw on the underside in the forward tip of the magazine housing. Remove the guard and magazine housing downward, and the action upward.

16. The magazine floorplate latch is its own spring, and is retained on the rear of the magazine housing by a single screw. Remove the screw, and take off the latch downward.

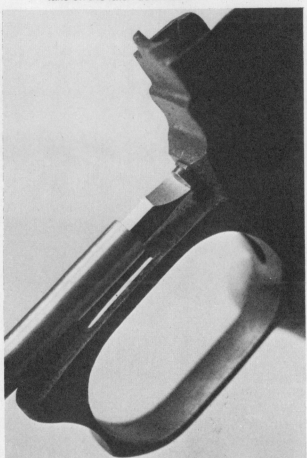

17. The combination ejector and feed interruptor is located on the left side of the receiver, and is secured by a screw at the rear. On some early guns, the ejector and interruptor/spring are two separate parts. Remove the screw, then check the next step.

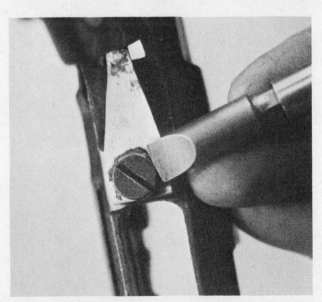

18. In addition to the screw, the ejector/interruptor is also dovetail-mounted, and must be drifted forward and sprung slightly outward at the front for removal.

19. The combination trigger spring and bolt stop is retained on the underside of the receiver by a large vertical screw. Remove the screw. The part will be loose, but is not removed at this time.

20. Drift out the trigger cross-pin, and remove the trigger and bolt stop/spring downward.

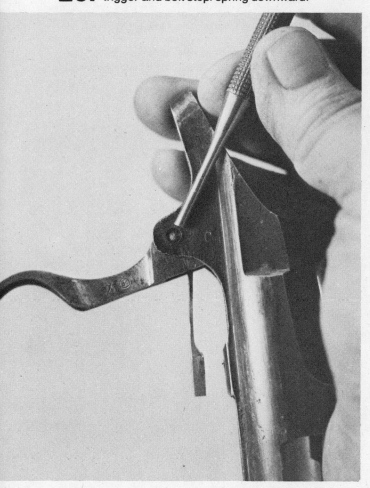

Reassembly Tips:

1. When turning the striker back into the cocking piece, turn it until snug, but do not over-tighten it. If necessary, back it off until the groove in the rear tip of the striker shaft aligns with the groove in the rear face of the cocking knob, as shown.

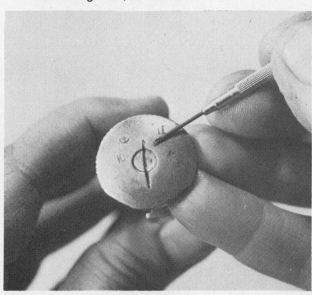

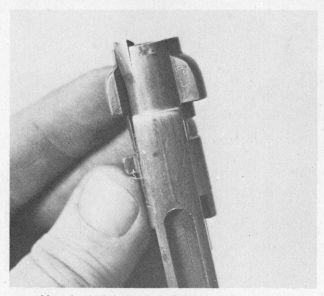

2. After the bolt head is installed on the connector, it must be turned to the position shown before the bolt head and connector are put back on the bolt.

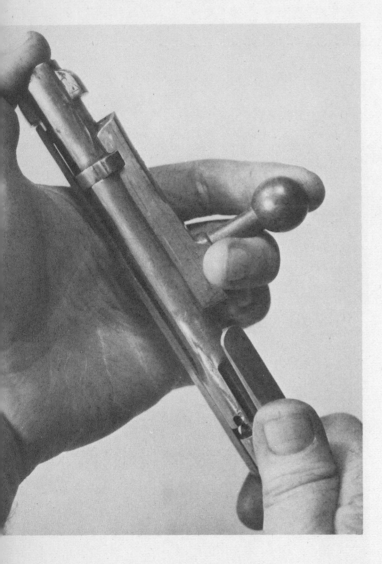

3. When replacing the connector and bolt head on the bolt, keep the bolt head pushed toward the rear, as shown, while turning the cocking knob to bring the lug on the connector back into its recess. When this movement is completed, the bolt will be cocked, and ready for re-insertion in the receiver.

MOSSBERG MODEL 479

Data:	Mossberg Model 479
Origin:	United States
Manufacturer:	O. F. Mossberg & Sons North Haven, Connecticut
Cartridges:	30-30 and 35 Remington
Magazine capacity:	6 rounds
Over-all length:	38½ inches
Barrel length:	20 inches
Weight:	7½ pounds

The original version of this gun, the Model 472, was first offered in 1973. About a year ago (1979), a slight redesign changed the designation to Model 479. With different model numbers, the gun has also been made for Western Auto Stores and Montgomery Ward. Mechanically, all of these are essentially the same, and the instructions will apply. The two most notable features are the manual hammer-block safety and the mounting of the trigger in the lever, rather than in the receiver.

Disassembly:

1. The lever pivot cross-pin is retained by a plunger and spring inside its mount. Open the action about half-way, and use a non-marring punch to drift out the lever pivot in either direction. Remove the lever downward.

2. The trigger is retained in the lever by a roll cross-pin. When drifting out the pin, take care to restrain the trigger spring and plunger, and ease them out. The trigger is removed downward, into the interior of the guard.

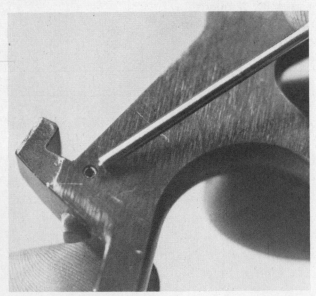

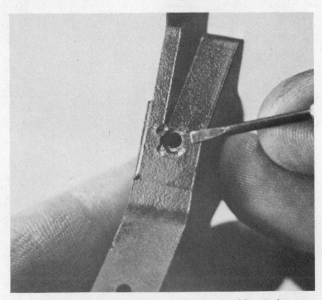

3. The lever latch plunger and spring are retained by a roll cross-pin. The spring is quite strong, so restrain the parts and ease them out.

4. The lever pivot retaining plunger and its spring are retained in their hole above the pivot hole by a stake mark at the edge of the hole. Removal is not recommended in normal disassembly. If necessary for repair, insert a tapered drift punch to expand the staked edge to the side.

5. Removal of the lever will release the bolt, and it can be taken out toward the rear. Holding the hammer back beyond its normal full-cock position will ease bolt removal.

6. Drifting out the vertical roll pin at the rear of the bolt will release the striker and its spring for removal toward the rear.

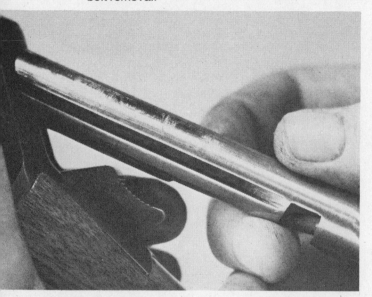

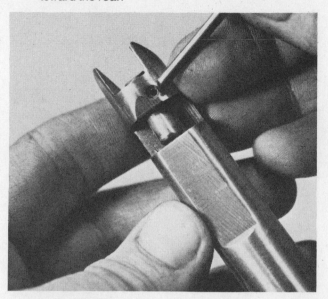

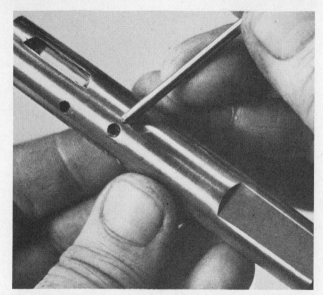

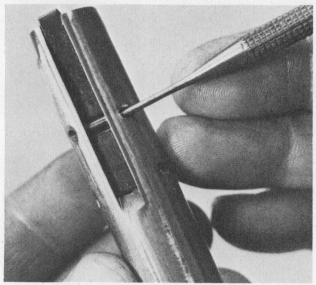

7. The firing pin is retained by a vertical roll pin on the right side of the bolt, just to the rear of the extractor. The firing pin is removed toward the rear.

8. The extractor, which is its own spring, is retained on the right side of the bolt by a vertical pin on the right side of the bolt. Drifting out the pin will allow removal of the extractor toward the right.

9. Push the ejector mounting stud out of its hole in the left side of the receiver, and remove the ejector and its attached spring from inside. The spring is staked in place, and should be removed only for breakage replacement.

10. The buttstock is retained by a through-bolt from the rear. The bolt head is not deep in the stock, and after removal of the buttplate an ordinary large screwdriver can be used. Remove the bolt, and take off the stock toward the rear.

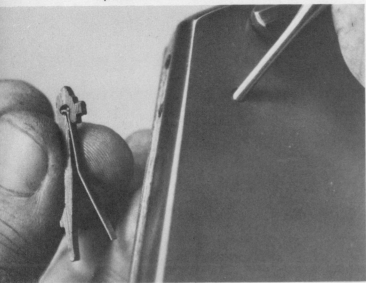

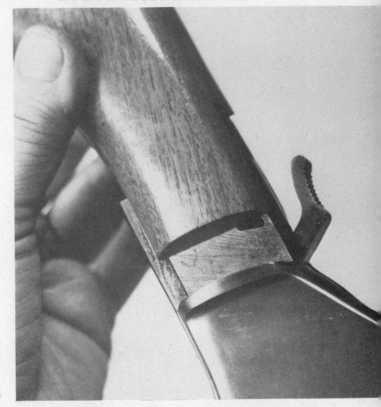

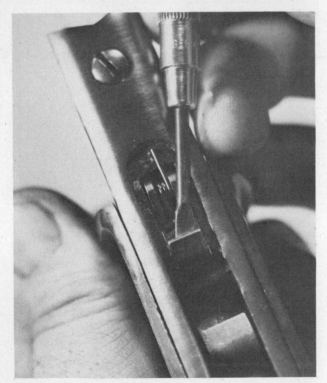

11. Restrain the hammer, and insert a screwdriver to pull the front of the sear downward. Ease the hammer down to the fired position.

12. With large parallel pliers or a wrench of proper size, unscrew the hammer spring housing and remove it from the rear of the receiver, along with the spring and plunger it contains.

13. Remove the vertical screw on the underside at the forward end of the sub-frame.

14. Remove the vertical screw at the rear of the sub-frame.

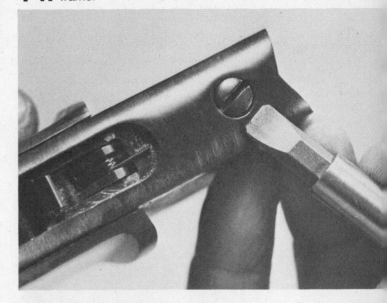

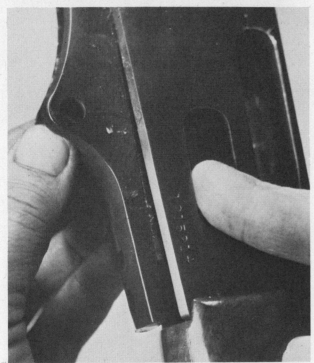

15. With the carrier (lifter) in lowered position, push in the loading gate until it clears its opening in the receiver. Move the sub-frame downward a short distance, just clear of the receiver.

16. Insert a tool to depress the bolt locking block to its full upward position, and hold it there. Move the sub-frame toward the front and downward, and remove it from the receiver. Take care that the gate does not drag on the inside of the receiver as this is done. As the sub-frame is removed, the hammer strut (rebound lever) will drop out at the rear, so take care that it isn't lost.

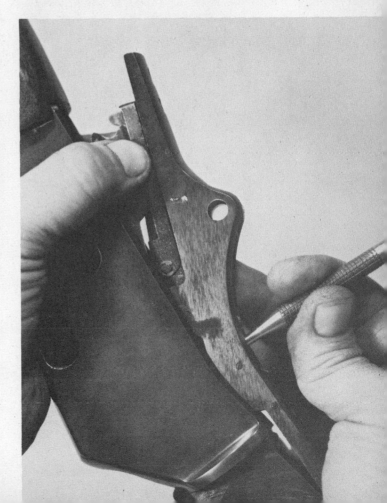

17. Remove the locking block and its spring from the bottom of the receiver.

18. Push out the hammer pivot, and remove the hammer upward.

19. Removal of the hammer will allow the sear to pivot upward, relieving tension on its spring. Push out the sear cross-pin, and remove the sear and its spring.

20. Remove the loading gate toward the right. The loading gate mounting post is also the pivot for the carrier.

21. Remove the carrier upward.

22. Restrain the carrier plunger, and remove the C-clip on the right side of the carrier. Remove the plunger and spring toward the left.

23. Use an Allen wrench to take out the safety retaining screw, located inside the receiver on the right side.

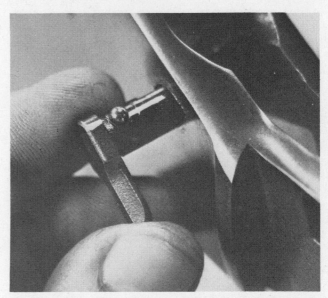

24. Remove the safety lever toward the left. **Caution:** *As the safety detent ball clears the left side of the receiver, its spring will force it out of its hole in the safety. Restrain the ball, and take care that it isn't lost.*

25. Remove the vertical screw on the underside of the magazine tube at its forward end, restraining the end plug against the tension of the magazine spring. Take out the end plug, magazine spring, and follower.

26. Remove the screw in the top of the front sight, and take off the sight upward.

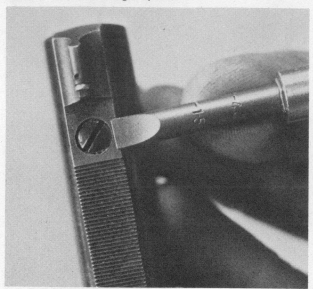

27. Remove the cross-screw in the front barrel band, and slide the barrel band off toward the front.

28. Remove the cross-screw in the rear barrel band, and slide the band off toward the front. The magazine tube can now be taken out toward the front, and the fore-end wood can be removed.

Reassembly Tips:

1. When replacing the sear and sear spring, note that the L-shaped end of the spring goes toward the front, as shown.

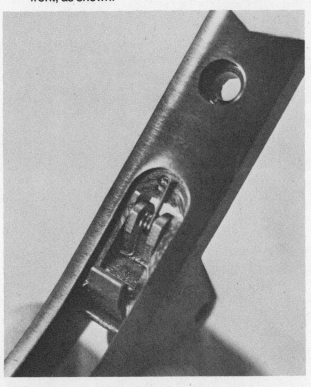

2. When replacing the sub-frame in the receiver, note that the hammer strut must be inserted before the sub-frame is moved into the receiver. Also note that the bolt locking block must be depressed to its full top position and held there while the sub-frame is put in.

3. Grip the ejector with sharp-nosed pliers and guide its mounting stud into the hole in the left wall of the receiver. when it is in place, insert a fingertip to hold it there while the bolt is started in from the rear.

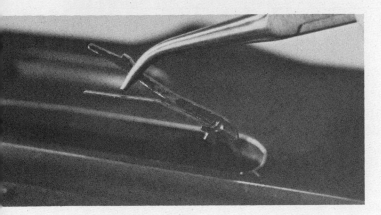

REMINGTON MODEL 8

Data: Remington Model 8
Origin: United States
Manufacturer: Remington Arms Company
Ilion, New York
Cartridges: 25, 30, 32, and 35 Remington
Magazine capacity: 5 rounds
Over-all length: 41½ inches
Barrel length: 22 inches
Weight: 8½ pounds

Designed by the great John M. Browning in 1900, the Model 8 was the first successful centerfire autoloading rifle made in America. Produced by Remington from 1906 to 1936, the Model 8 has the classic Browning long-recoil locking system, with the barrel and bolt recoiling together during the moment of high pressure. The gun was very slightly re-designed in 1936 to become the Model 81, and was made in that form until 1950. Except for very minor features, the two guns are mechanically identical, and the instructions can generally be used for both.

Disassembly:

1. Move the safety to the off-safe position (downward) and pull back on the operating handle until the bolt locks open. Remove the screw on the underside of the fore-end, and take off the fore-end downward and toward the front.

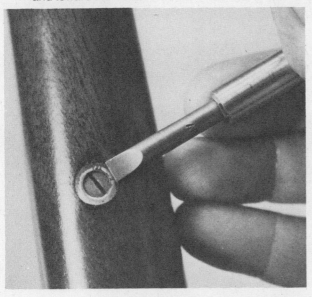

2. Swing out the takedown lever, and unscrew the barrel retaining bolt.

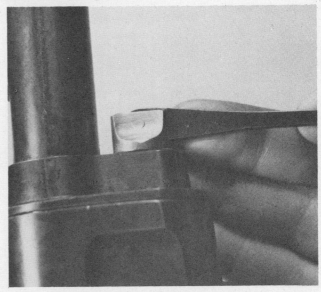

3. Remove the barrel assembly toward the front. If necessary, the barrel retaining bolt can be moved forward and unscrewed from the barrel housing. The takedown lever is cross-pinned to the bolt.

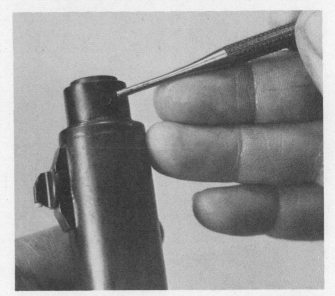

4. A special spanner wrench was once available to remove the barrel nut. If you do not have the wrench, grip the protruding rear portion of the barrel in a padded vise, and insert a drift punch in the wrench holes in the barrel nut, tapping the side of the punch to nudge the nut around. Unscrew the nut, and remove it. (Turn it counter-clockwise, front view.)

5. After the nut is taken off, remove the barrel toward the rear.

6. The handle of the original wrench was used to remove the barrel jacket bushing, but any steel plate of suitable thickness will do this. Unscrew the bushing counter-clockwise (front view). **Caution:** *Removal of the bushing will release the powerful recoil spring and buffer spring, so control the bushing as it nears the end of its threads, and ease it out.* Remove the bushing, the barrel nut washer, the recoil spring and its case, and the buffer spring toward the front. The jacket plug, the base for the springs inside the jacket, is *not* removed.

7. Restrain the bolt handle, trip the bolt latch, and ease the bolt to its forward position. Remove the vertical screw at the rear tip of the lower tang, and take off the stock toward the rear. If the stock is tight, bump the front of the comb with the heel of the hand to start it.

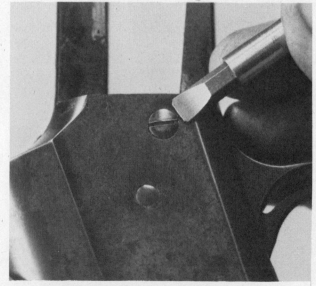

8. Remove the trigger group cross-screw, at the lower edge of the receiver on the left side.

9. Drift out the small cross-pin near the bolt release.

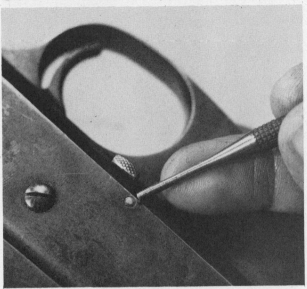

10. Remove the trigger and magazine group downward and toward the rear.

11. Move the magazine housing upward out of the trigger group. If it is very tight, tap it gently with a rubber hammer to start it.

12. The magazine should be disassembled only if absolutely necessary. Use a tool to tilt the follower to the side, freeing it from the front flanges. Then, when the front is clear, move the follower toward the front, tilt the follower again, and remove it toward the side. The spring can then be removed.

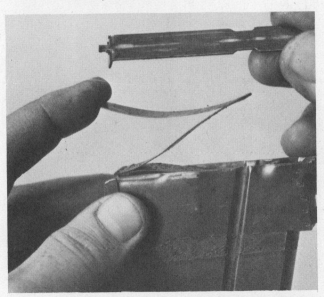

13. Restrain the hammer, pull the trigger, and ease the hammer down, relieving the tension of the hammer spring. Push out the hammer pivot, and take off the hammer upward. Use a roll pin punch to remove the hollow pivot, to avoid damage.

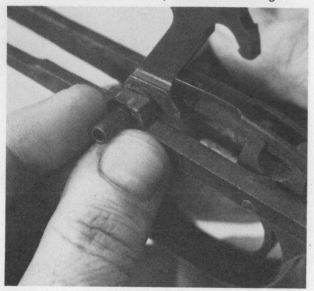

14. Remove the hammer spring screw, located on the underside of the lower tang, and take off the spring upward.

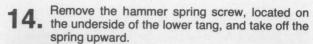

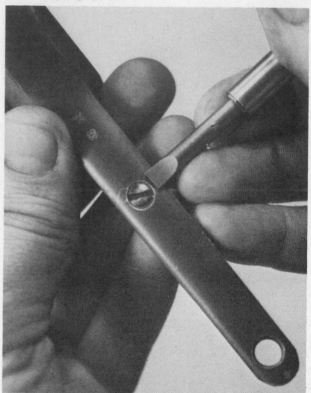

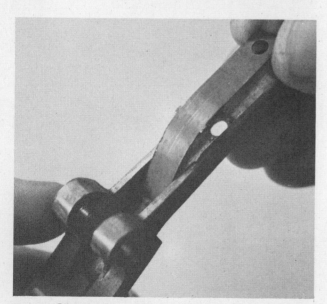

15. Slide the trigger spring straight to the rear, climbing its side studs up the ramp slots inside the tang, and remove the spring toward the rear.

16. Drift out the trigger cross-pin, and remove the trigger upward.

17. Push out the cross-pin at the rear of the action spring tube, and remove the spring plug, action spring, and follower toward the rear. **Caution:** *The spring is under tension, so control the plug and ease it out.*

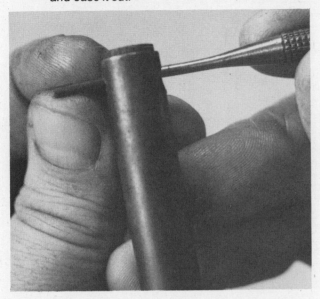

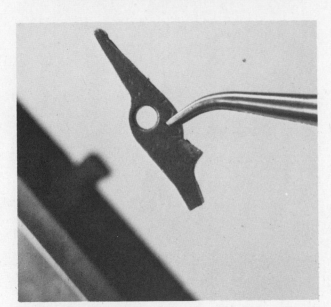

19. Move the bolt to the rear, and move the bolt carrier latch off its post inside the receiver, and remove the latch.

20. Move the barrel lock and its attached spring off its post inside the receiver, and remove it downward.

18. Detach the lower arm of the bolt carrier latch spring from its screw-stud inside the receiver, pivot the spring to the rear, and remove it from its post.

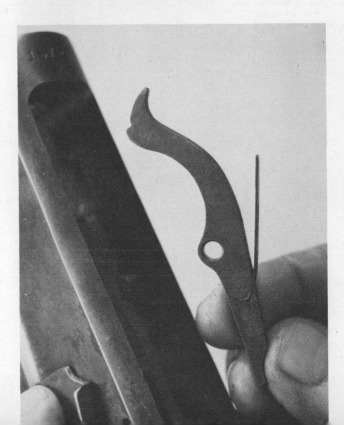

21. Move the bolt release (magazine indicator) assembly off its post inside the receiver, and remove it. This assembly includes an attached spring and the release thumbpiece, the latter being semi-riveted on the latch, and *not removed* in normal takedown.

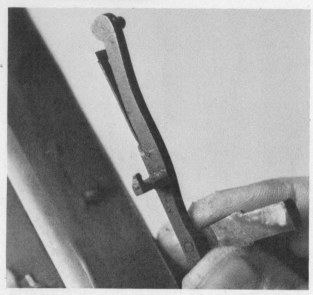

22. With the bolt still in the rear position, turn the safety lever downward beyond its normal off-safe position, until it is pointing downward, in the position shown, and push the safety cross-piece toward the right. Remove the safety lever and cross-piece from the right side.

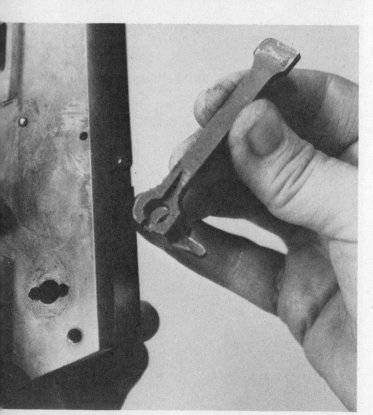

23. Remove the safety rocker from inside the receiver.

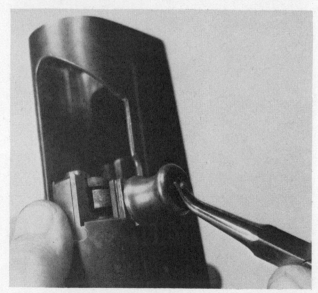

24. Pull the small knob at the center of the bolt handle outward, and hold it out while the handle is slid forward out of its recess in the bolt. Note that the bolt should be in the position shown, to allow the handle to be aligned with the access cut in the receiver. Remove the handle toward the right. The handle latch system can be removed by unscrewing the retaining bushing inside the handle, but this will require a special shop-made twin-point tool.

25. The bolt assembly can now be removed toward the front.

26. Drift out the link pin at the lower rear of the bolt, and take off the link toward the rear.

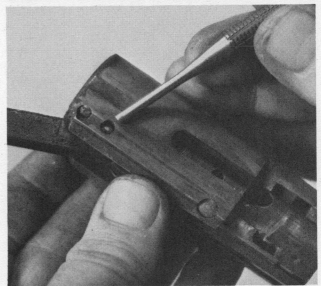

27. Drift out the firing pin retaining pin, located at the extreme lower rear of the bolt on the right side. Note that the pin angles upward toward the left, and is driven out upward. Remove the firing pin and its return spring toward the rear.

28. Insert a screwdriver into the bolt carrier from the front to lift the upper cam pin out of its track, and remove it. Repeat this operation with the cam pin on the lower right of the carrier.

29. The bolt lock is retained on the left side of the carrier by a vertical pin, and only half of the pin tip is accessible on the underside of the carrier, so a very slim drift punch must be used to drive the pin out upward. Remove the bolt lock and its spring.

30. Move the bolt and extractor forward out of the carrier. After it clears its track in the carrier, the extractor is easily detached.

Reassembly Tips:

Strange as it may seem, considering its large number of parts, reassembly of the Model 8 has no difficult points. The gun is so beautifully designed that it is not possible to replace any parts improperly. A careful reversal of the disassembly procedure is all that's required.

31. The ejector is retained by a cross-pin at the front of the bolt. Drifting out the pin will free the ejector and its spring toward the front. **Caution:** *The spring is under tension, so restrain the ejector and ease it out.*

REMINGTON MODEL 600

Data:	Remington Model 600
Origin:	United States
Manufacturer:	Remington Arms Company Bridgeport, Connecticut
Cartridges:	222, 243, 6mm, 308, 35, 6.5mm Remington Magnum and 350 Remington Magnum
Magazine capacity:	4, 5 or 6 rounds, depending on caliber
Over-all length:	37¼ inches
Barrel length:	18½ inches
Weight:	5½ pounds

This handy little carbine, and its counterpart, the Model 660, did not stay long on the scene. The Model 600, with its distinctive ventilated barrel rib, was made from 1964 to 1967. The successor, the Model 660, was made from 1968 to 1971. During this time, a version called the "Mohawk 600" was produced, a gun very similar to the Model 660, but without the barrel rib. Mechanically, these three are virtually identical, and the same instructions will apply.

Disassembly:

1. Open the bolt and move it part-way to the rear. Use a small tool to depress the bolt stop, located at the left rear of the receiver on the inside, next to the bolt. Hold the stop down, and remove the bolt toward the rear. As the bolt emerges from the receiver, it must be lifted to clear its right lug over the safety.

2. Grip the underlug of the cocking piece firmly in a vise, and pull the bolt forward until a gap appears between the front of the cocking piece and the rear of the bolt endpiece. Insert a thin piece of steel plate between the cocking piece and the bolt endpiece. Note that on some models, such as the one shown, a slot is provided on the side of the cocking piece for the insertion of the plate. Release the spring tension, and the plate will trap the striker at the rear.

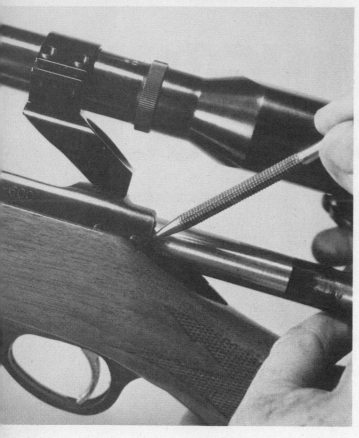

3. Taking care not to dislodge the plate, unscrew the bolt endpiece from the rear of the bolt. The factory advises against further disassembly of the striker system, since reassembly can be difficult without special tools. I will note here that the cocking piece is retained on the rear of the striker shaft by a cross-pin.

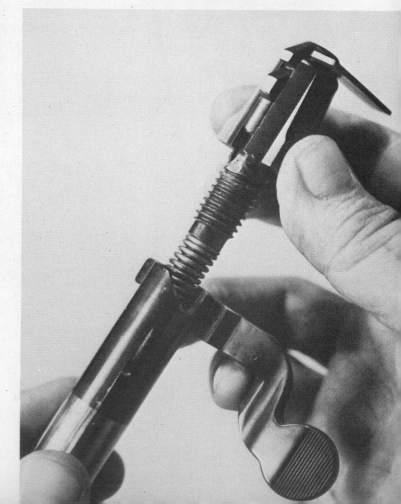

4. The ejector is retained in the front of the bolt by a cross-pin. Restrain the ejector when drifting out the pin, and remove the ejector and spring toward the front.

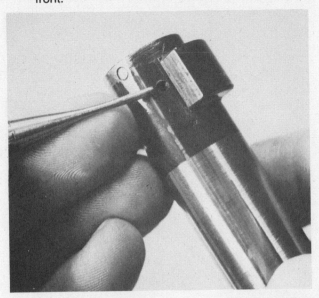

5. The extractor is retained inside the bolt face recess by a small rivet, and if unbroken it should not be removed. If removal is necessary, the rivet is driven inward. The ejector must first be removed.

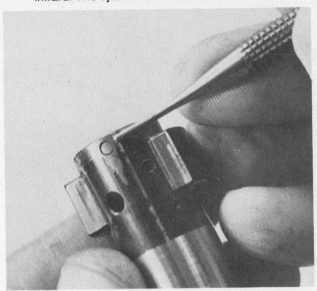

6. Remove the large screw on the underside at the front of the trigger guard/magazine housing. Remove the screw on the underside at the rear of the trigger guard, and separate the action from the stock. The trigger guard unit can be taken off downward.

7. The magazine box is easily detached from the underside of the receiver, and the spring and follower can be taken out of the box.

8. Position the safety snap washer so its opening is aligned with the stud on the detent spring, and push off the snap washer upward. Take off the detent spring, and take care not to lose the small steel ball in the side of the safety lever beneath the spring.

9. Push out the safety pivot toward the left, and remove the safety toward the rear and downward.

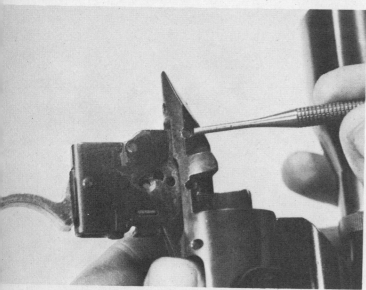

10. Drift out the rear trigger housing cross-pin toward the left, while restraining the sear at the top. When the pin is out, the sear spring will push the sear upward.

11. Drift out the front trigger housing cross-pin, and remove the trigger housing downward.

13. The trigger housing should not be disassembled beyond this point in normal takedown. There are three trigger adjustment screws, two at the front and one at the rear, which are set and sealed with lacquer at the factory, and these should not be disturbed. A cross-pin retains the trigger and its connector, but removal requires that the two front screws be backed out.

12. Remove the sear and sear spring from the top of the trigger housing.

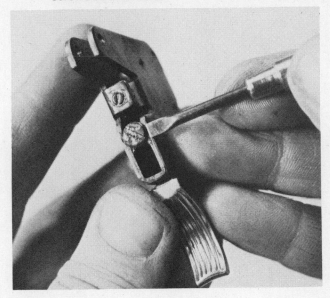

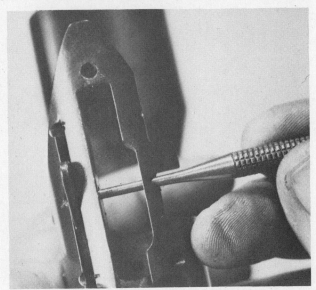

14. Removal of the bolt stop requires that its short pin be drifted out toward the left, and there is an access hole on the right side of the receiver through which a drift punch can be inserted to drive out the pin. The bolt stop and its spring are removed downward.

Reassembly Tips:

1. When replacing the trigger housing, start the two cross-pins in from the left, and be certain that the holes in the housing are aligned with the pins, to avoid deforming the housing. When the pins are just into the housing, but not into the center space, insert the sear from the rear, align its hole with the front cross-pin, and drive the pin across. Be sure the left tip of the cross-pin is clear of the bolt stop slot.

2. Insert the sear spring, being sure it is properly positioned to engage its recess on the underside of the sear, and swing the sear downward, keeping it depressed while the rear cross-pin is driven across.

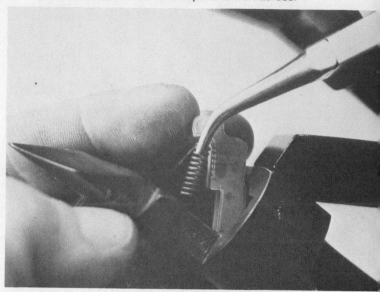

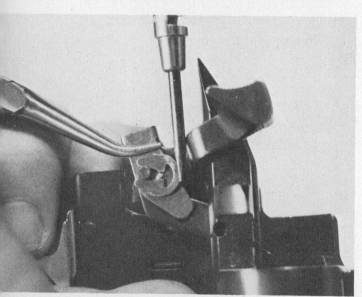

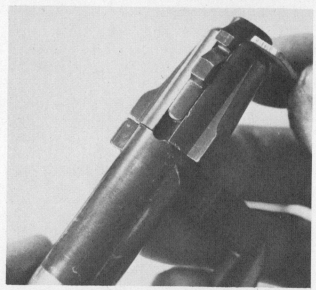

3. When replacing the safety system, be sure the pivot post is all the way through to the right when installing the detent spring and snap washer. Use pliers to compress the detent spring, and be sure the inside surfaces of the washer engage the groove in the top of the pivot post.

4. When removing the steel plate holding the striker, position the bolt endpiece as shown, so the released striker cocking piece will be in cocked position, and the bolt will be ready for re-insertion in the receiver.

REMINGTON MODEL 700

Data:	Remington Model 700
Origin:	United States
Manufacturer:	Remington Arms Company Bridgeport, Connecticut
Cartridges:	Most popular calibers from 222 to 458
Magazine capacity:	4 rounds (3 in magnum calibers)
Over-all length:	41½ to 44½ inches
Barrel length:	22 or 24 inches
Weight:	7 to 7½ pounds

When Remington discontinued the Model 721, 722, and 725 rifles in 1962, the successor was the excellent Model 700. Although the basic mechanical features were essentially the same, there were a number of small mechanical improvements. Since its introduction, the Model 700 has been offered in several sub-models, each having various special features. From a takedown viewpoint, the only notable difference would be the version with a blind magazine, lacking a separate magazine floorplate. Otherwise, the same instructions will apply.

Disassembly:

1. Open the bolt, and push upward on the bolt release, located inside the trigger guard, just forward of the trigger. Remove the bolt toward the rear.

2. Grip the underlug of the cocking piece firmly in a vise, and pull the bolt body toward the front to clear the front projection of the cocking piece from the rear of the bolt. Unscrew the bolt from the sleeve and striker assembly counter-clockwise (front view).

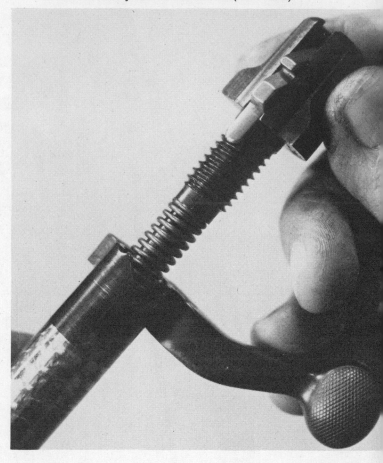

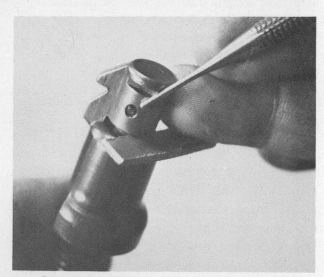

3. Grip the front portion of the striker firmly in a vise, taking care to exert no side pressure, and push the bolt sleeve forward until a small piece of steel (at least 1/16-inch thickness) can be inserted between the front of the cocking piece and the rear of the sleeve. Grip the cocking piece in a vise, hold firmly to the striker and spring, and drift out the cross-pin in the cocking piece. **Caution:** *The striker spring is fully compressed, and is quite strong, so keep it under control.* When the pin is out, slowly release the spring tension, and remove the striker, spring, and bolt sleeve toward the front.

4. Drifting out the cross-pin at the front of the bolt will release the ejector and its spring for removal toward the front. **Caution:** *The ejector spring is partially compressed, even when at rest. Control it, and ease it out.*

5. The extractor is retained inside the cartridge head recess in the front face of the bolt by a tiny rivet, and removal in normal disassembly is definitely *not* recommended, as this will usually break the extractor. If removal is necessary to replace a broken extractor, use a small-diameter drift punch to drive the rivet inward. Note that the ejector *must* be removed before this is done.

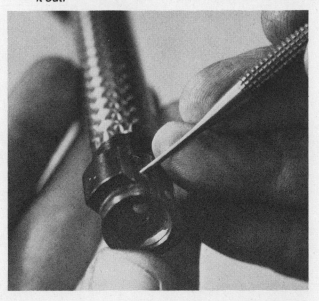

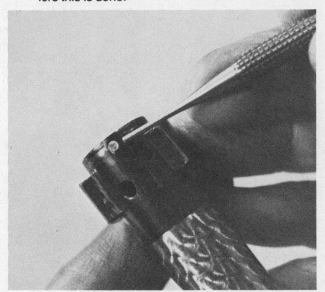

6. Remove the large vertical screw at the rear of the trigger guard. Remove the large vertical screw on the underside of the stock, forward of the trigger guard. Remove the vertical screw at the front of the trigger guard, and take the action out of the stock upward. The trigger guard can be taken off downward.

7. The magazine spring and follower will be released for removal as the action is taken out of the stock. The magazine box is retained by a small vertical screw through a tab at the rear, on the right underside of the receiver.

8. Drift out the front trigger housing cross-pin toward the right.

9. Note that the rear trigger housing cross-pin is also the retainer and pivot for the bolt stop and its spring, and the spring should be restrained while the pin is drifted out.

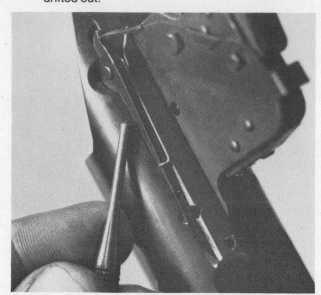

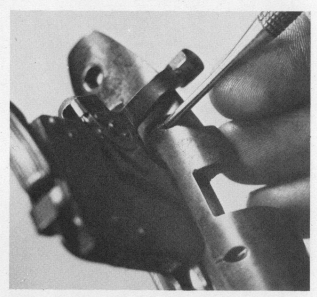

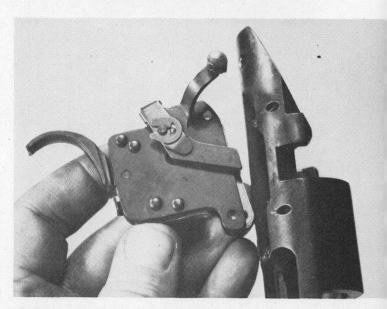

10. Set the safety lever in the on-safe position, and drift out the rear trigger housing cross-pin. Remember that the bolt stop and its spring will be released as the pin clears their position.

11. Remove the trigger housing downward.

12. Remove the bolt stop and its spring.

13. Remove the sear and its spring from the top of the trigger housing.

14. Remove the C-clip from the end of the safety pivot post on the right side of the housing, and take out the pivot post toward the left. The safety detent spring can then be pivoted downward and removed. Take care not to lose the small detent ball, which will be released as the spring is removed. The safety can now be moved out toward the rear. Removal of the pivot post will also free the bolt stop release from the left side of the housing.

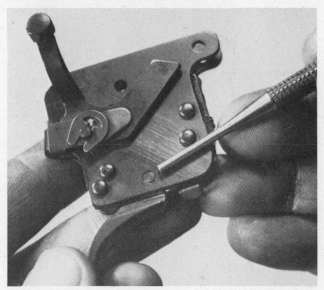

15. Drifting out the trigger cross-pin will release the trigger and trigger connector for removal. The other four cross-pins hold the housing together, and are riveted in place. Removal of these pins is not recommended.

Reassembly Tips:

1. Before the bolt can be replaced in the receiver, the striker must be in the cocked position, as shown.

2. If a broken extractor is being replaced, a new extractor rivet should be used. Clinching the new rivet is difficult, as its inner head must be well supported while the outer tip is peened and spread. With a new tool from B-square, shown in the photo, the job is much less difficult.

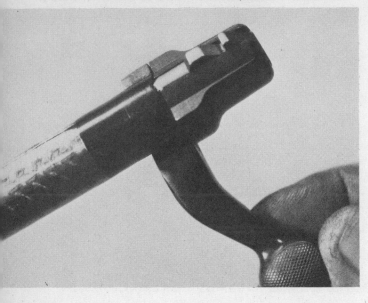

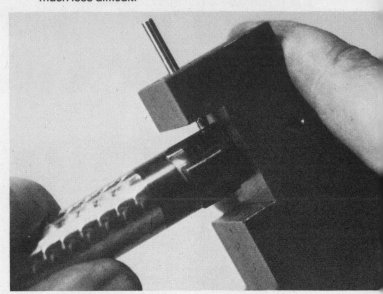

REMINGTON MODEL 742

Data:	Remington Model 742
Origin:	United States
Manufacturer:	Remington Arms Company Bridgeport, Connecticut
Cartridges:	6mm Rem., 243 Win., 280 Rem., 308 Win., 30-06
Magazine capacity:	4 rounds
Over-all length:	42 inches
Barrel length:	22 inches
Weight:	7½ pounds

The original version of this gun, the Model 740, was first offered in 1955, and was made for only five years. It was redesigned in 1960 to become the Model 742, and in this form it is still in production. A carbine version is also available, with an 18½-inch barrel. Like its ancestor, the Model 740, the 742 is a difficult gun to take down. For simple repairs, such as a broken extractor or firing pin, the gun must be totally disassembled, including pulling the barrel. There are a few mechanical differences in the older Model 740, but otherwise the instructions can apply to certain shared systems.

Disassembly:

1. Remove the magazine, and cycle the action to cock the internal hammer. Push the safety across to the on-safe position. Use a drift punch to push out the two cross-pins in the receiver.

2. Move the trigger group forward, then take it off downward.

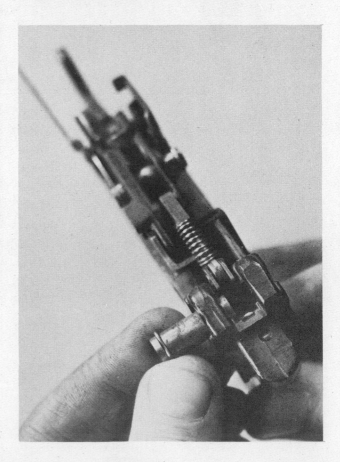

3. Push the safety to the off-safe position. Restrain the hammer, pull the trigger to release it, and ease it forward. Keeping the trigger pulled to the rear, push out the rear cross-pin sleeve toward the left.

4. Removal of the pin sleeve will allow the top of the trigger to move further toward the rear, easing the tension of the combination sear and trigger spring. This spring can now be flexed off its stud on the rear of the sear, and removed upward.

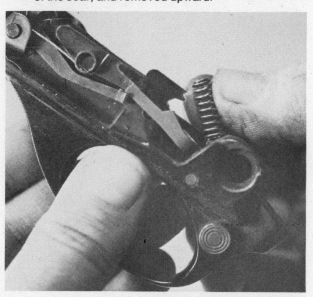

5. Drift out the trigger cross-pin toward the right.

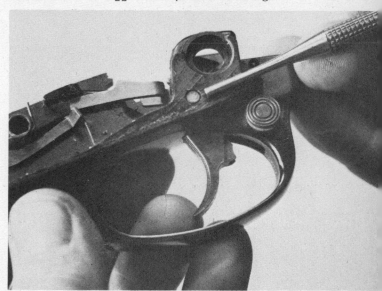

6. Remove the trigger assembly upward, turning it slightly to allow its left connector arm to clear the shelf on the trigger housing.

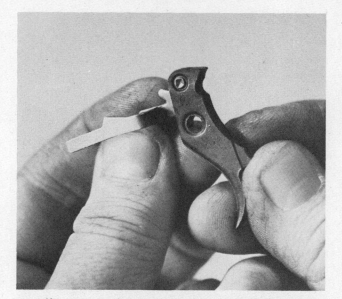

7. If necessary for repair, the right and left connector arms can be detached from the trigger by drifting out the cross-pin. However, its left tip is semi-riveted on the left side, and in normal disassembly it is best left in place. If removal is necessary, the pin must be drifted out toward the right, and take care that the parts are well-supported, to avoid deforming the top wings of the trigger.

8. Push out the small cross-pin at the upper rear of the trigger housing toward the right, holding a fingertip over the hole on top to restrain the released safety spring.

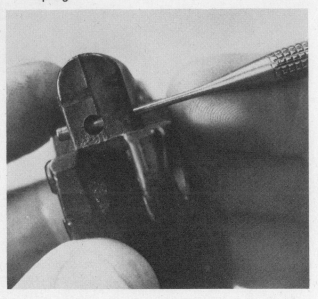

9. Remove the safety spring from its hole in the top, and, if possible, the detent ball beneath it. If the ball can't be shaken out at this time, it can be removed after the safety is taken out. Push out the safety toward either side, and if the detent ball has not been previously removed, insert a small drift into the hole at the top, and push the ball downward, into the safety tunnel. Take care to catch it as it rolls out.

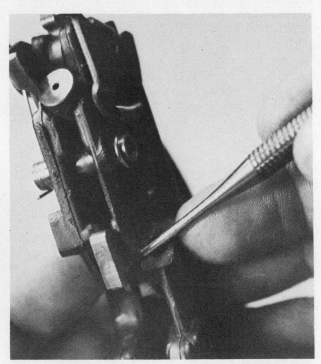

10. The sear pivot pin is accessible on the right side of the trigger housing by angling a small drift punch as shown. After it is started out it can be removed toward the left. The sear is then taken out upward.

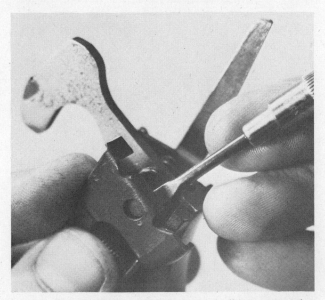

11. The magazine catch is moved off its post on the trigger housing toward the right for removal. **Caution:** *The catch spring is compressed even when at rest, so control it during removal.* If the catch is very tight, it may have to be pried gently off its post.

12. Unhook the disconnector spring from its slot in the left end of the front cross-pin sleeve, and push out the sleeve toward the right.

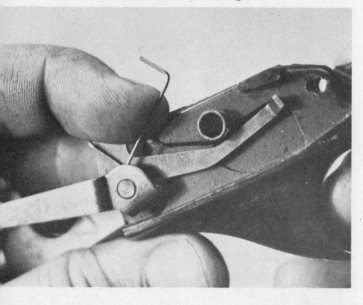

13. Pull the hammer back to slightly depress the hammer spring plunger, and relieve tension on the disconnector, and push the hammer and disconnector pivot pin toward the right, just far enough to clear the disconnector.

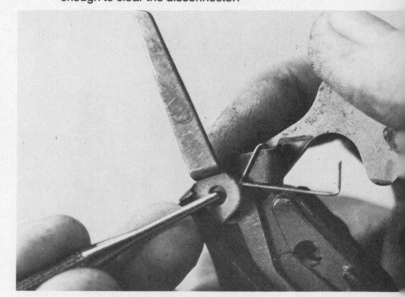

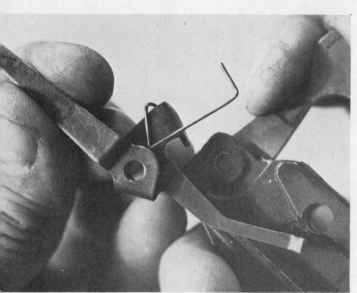

14. Remove the disconnector and its spring. Keep a firm grip on the hammer during this operation, with its spring plunger slightly depressed. The disconnector spring is easily separated from the disconnector after the part is removed.

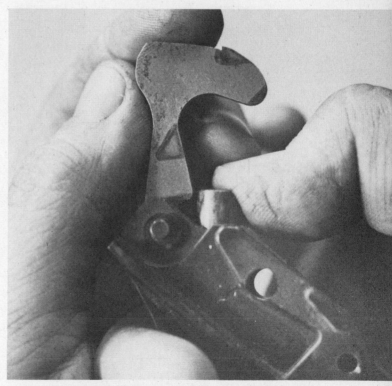

15. Ease the hammer forward while holding and restraining the plunger, slowly releasing the tension of the spring.

16. Push the hammer pivot pin out toward the right, and take off the hammer. Remove the hammer plunger and spring from their recess in the trigger housing.

17. The buttstock is retained by a through-bolt from the rear, accessible by taking off the buttplate. Use a B-Square stock tool or a large screwdriver to unscrew the bolt, and remove the stock toward the rear. Take care not to lose the stock bearing plate, mounted between the stock and the receiver. The fore-end is retained by a large screw in its forward tip. Remove the screw, and take off the fore-end cap. The fore-end can then be slid forward and off.

18. Use a roll pin punch to drift out the action tube support pin, the large cross-pin in the gas tube housing.

19. Draw the bolt all the way to the rear, and move the action tube support bracket back off the gas tube housing. Tip the action tube downward, and slide it toward the front when it has cleared the lower edge of the gas tube housing. Take care not to release the bolt at this time, as it is very important to avoid damage to the gas tube.

20. Release the bolt very slowly as the action tube is withdrawn, easing the tension of the recoil spring. Remove the recoil spring from the rear of the action bar sleeve. It will still have some tension, so control it and ease it out.

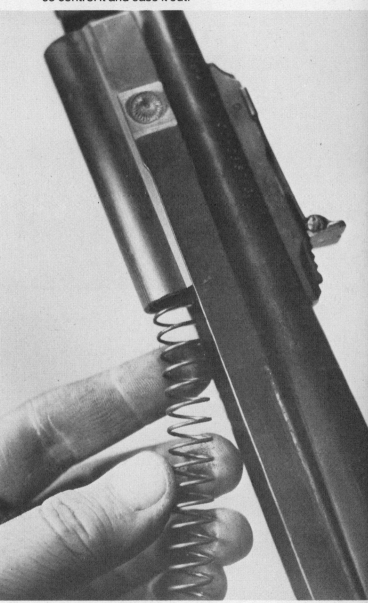

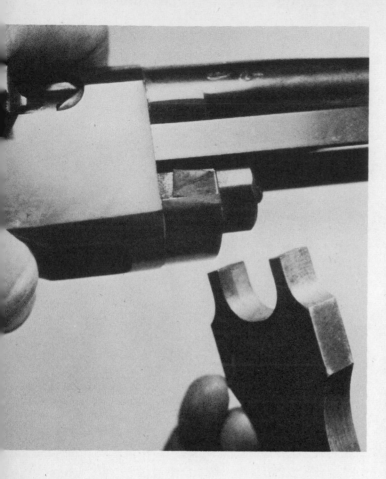

21a. With a Brownells wrench, as shown, or an open-end wrench of the proper size, turn the barrel nut counter-clockwise (front view) and remove it. Take off the fore-end stabilizer spring, mounted behind the nut.

21b. If the barrel nut has never been removed, it will be quite tight, and it may be necessary to rap the wrench handle with a hammer to start the nut.

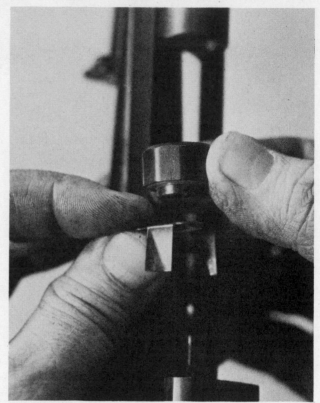

22. Move the bolt partially toward the rear to clear its locking lugs from the barrel, and move the barrel forward out of the receiver. Move the bolt back to the front, to allow space between the action bars, and turn the barrel at a right angle to the receiver to clear its underlug projections from the action bars. Lift the barrel straight up and out of the action bars.

23. Position the bolt handle and the ejection port cover to give access to the bolt handle retaining pin, and drive out the pin downward. Remove the bolt handle toward the right.

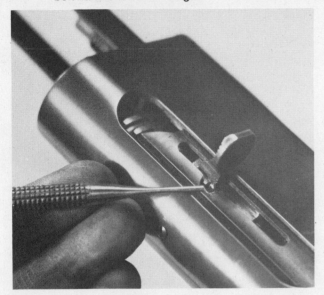

24. Remove the bolt and action bar assembly toward the front, taking off the ejection port cover as it emerges from the receiver.

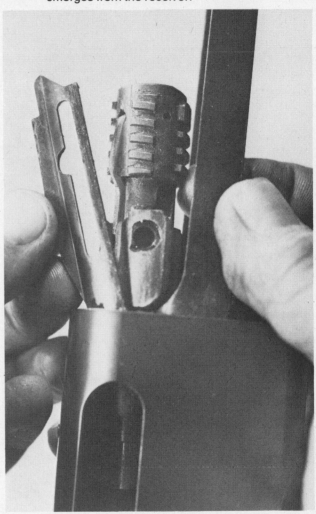

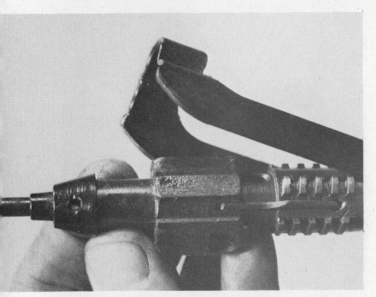

25. The bolt is easily detached from the action bar assembly by moving it downward, turning it slightly, and taking it off toward the rear.

26. The firing pin is retained in the bolt by a cross-pin at the rear, and the firing pin and its return spring are removed toward the rear.

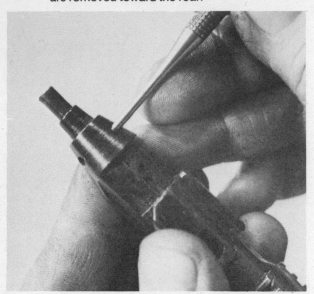

27. Insert a small screwdriver into the cam pin track at the front to lift the cam pin out of its hole in the bolt carrier. The bolt can then be separated from the carrier.

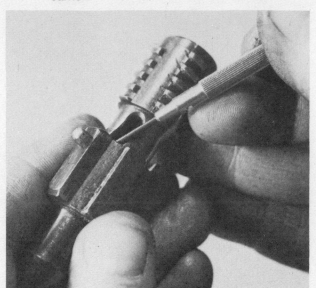

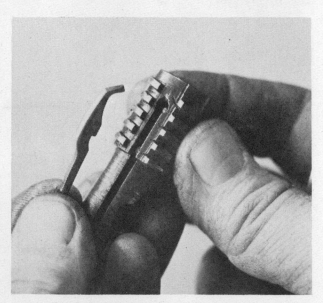

28. The bolt latch can now be moved toward the rear and upward for removal. Take care that the bolt latch pivot and plunger, and their springs, are not lost from their holes beneath the bolt latch—these are very small parts.

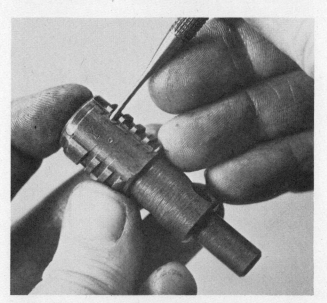

29. The ejector is removed by drifting out its cross-pin near the front of the bolt. **Caution:** *The ejector spring is quite strong, so restrain the ejector during removal, and ease it out.*

30. The extractor is mounted inside the cartridge head recess at the front of the bolt, and is held in place by a small rivet on the left side. Except for replacement of a broken extractor, this assembly should not be disturbed, as attempted removal will almost always break the extractor.

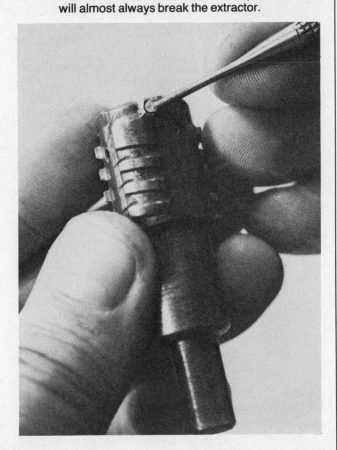

Reassembly Tips:

1. If the extractor has been removed for replacement of a broken one, installing and setting the new rivet can be very difficult, unless a tool such as the one shown is used. Newly available from B-Square, it is designed specifically for this job on all of the guns from Remington that have an extractor of this type.

2. When replacing the bolt carrier on the rear of the bolt, note that there is a notch on the carrier which must align with the tail of the bolt latch. The bolt latch must be depressed slightly as the parts are rejoined.

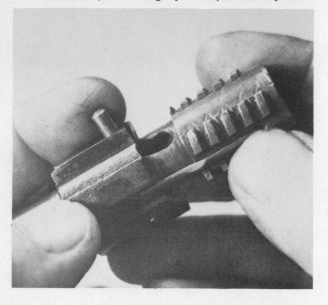

3. When replacing the bolt handle retaining pin, note that it has lengthwise stake marks at one end, and the opposite end should be inserted. Grip the pin with sharp-nosed pliers, insert it from inside the receiver, and drive it upward into place. Be sure the bolt handle is fully in place, and properly aligned with the hole, before driving in the pin.

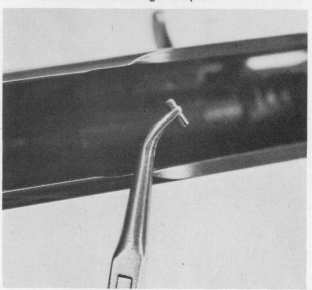

4. When replacing the barrel nut and fore-end stabilizer spring, be sure they are installed as shown, with the outer flanges of the stabilizer at the top, and the rebated nose of the barrel nut toward the rear.

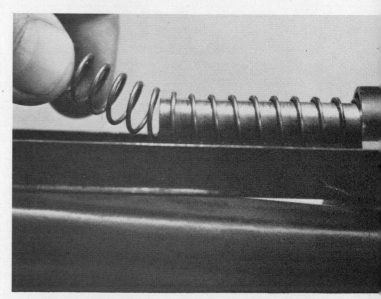

5. When replacing the recoil spring, partially insert the action tube, and slip the spring onto it from the rear, compressing the spring until its rear tip can be lifted onto its stud at the center of the barrel nut bolt. Then, push the action tube all the way to the rear. Once again, take care that the projecting gas tube is not damaged during replacement of the tube and its support bracket.

6. When replacing the front trigger group cross-pin sleeve, note that it must be oriented with its slot in the left end on the underside, so the disconnector spring can be hooked into the slot.

7. When replacing the safety spring, use a small screwdriver to depress the spring while inserting the cross-pin, pointed end first.

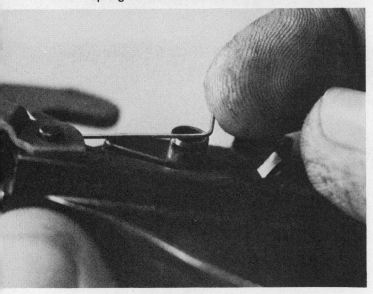

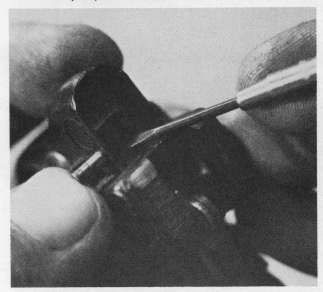

REMINGTON MODEL 760

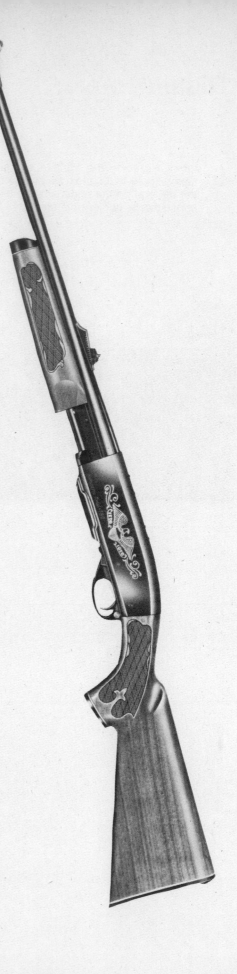

Data: Remington Model 760
Origin: United States
Manufacturer: Remington Arms Company
Bridgeport, Connecticut
Cartridges: A long list, from 222 to 30-06
Magazine capacity: 4 rounds
Over-all length: 42 inches
Barrel length: 22 inches
Weight: 7½ pounds

Before World War II, the design department at Remington was working on a replacement for the Model 141 slide-action rifle, something with a locking system that would handle modern high-pressure loads. This project was interrupted by the war, and when it was resumed afterward, the result was the Model 760 "Gamemaster" rifle, introduced in 1952. The gun is still in production. Many of its features were used in the semi-auto Model 740 and 742 rifles, and several parts will actually interchange.

Disassembly:

1. Remove the magazine, and cycle the action to cock the internal hammer. Push out the large and small cross-pins in the lower rear area of the receiver.

2. Move the trigger group forward, then remove it downward.

3. Grip the magazine catch firmly to control its spring tension, and push it off its post toward the right.

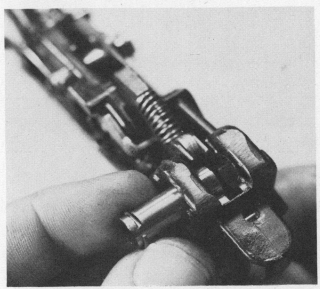

4. Restrain the hammer against the tension of its spring, and pull the trigger. Ease the hammer down beyond its normal fired position. The hammer spring plunger will be stopped by the inner arm of the disconnector. With the trigger still depressed, push out the rear cross-pin sleeve toward the left, and remove it.

5. Removal of the sleeve will allow the top of the trigger to move further toward the rear than its normal position, and will relieve the tension of the combination sear and trigger spring. Detach the spring from its stud on the back of the sear, and remove it upward.

6. Drift out the trigger pin toward the left, and remove it.

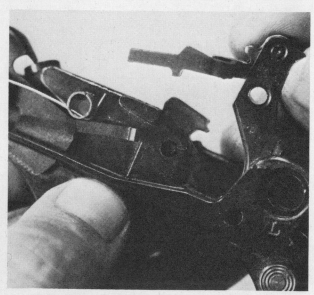

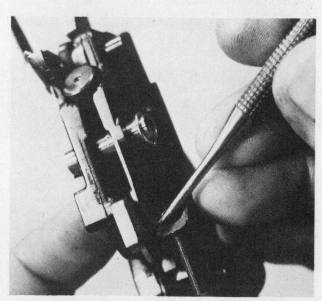

7. Remove the trigger and its attached connector arms upward. It will be necessary to turn the trigger slightly toward the left to clear the left arm past the upper shelf on the housing. The connector arms can be separated from the trigger by drifting out the cross-pin, but this is not advisable in normal takedown. If necessary for replacement of a broken arm, the pin must be drifted out toward the right.

8. The right end of the sear pin is accessible to an angled drift punch, and the pin is usually lightly staked on the left side. Nudge it toward the left, then use smooth-jawed pliers to remove it.

9. Remove the sear upward.

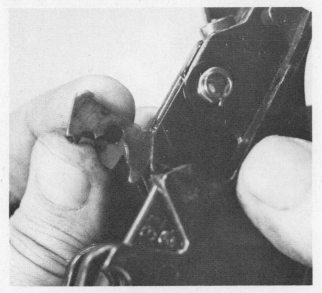

10. Unhook the rear arm of the action slide latch spring from its slot in the underside of the front guard cross-pin sleeve, and allow it to swing over forward, relieving its tension.

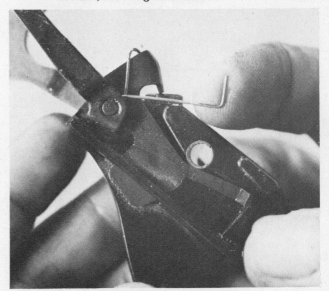

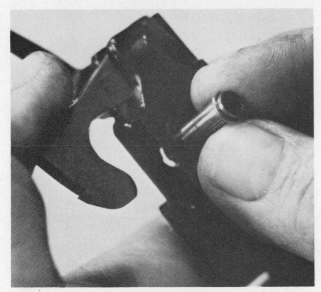

11. Depress the hammer spring plunger to relieve tension on the slide latch, and move its rear arm downward to clear the cross-pin sleeve. Remove the sleeve toward the right.

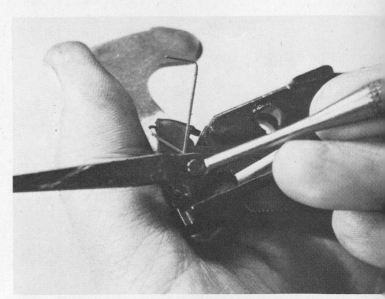

12. Push the hammer and latch pivot pin toward the right, just enough to clear the latch. During this operation, keep the hammer pushed back far enough to slightly depress the hammer spring plunger, taking pressure off the latch.

13. Keeping the hammer under control, remove the action slide latch and its spring upward.

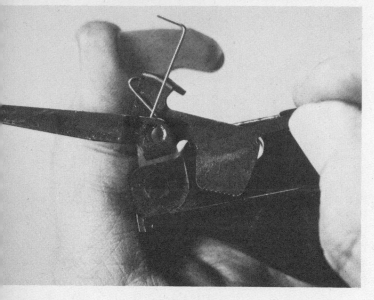

14. Restrain the hammer spring plunger, and ease the hammer over forward, slowly releasing the tension of the plunger and spring. Remove the plunger and spring upward and toward the front.

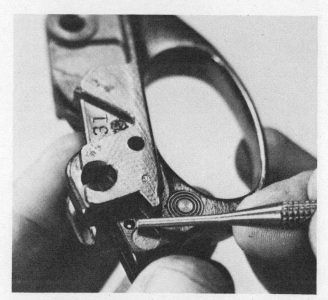

16. Push out the small cross-pin at the upper rear of the trigger group, holding a fingertip over the hole at the top to restrain the safety spring. Take out the spring upward. If the detent ball can be shaken out the top, remove it, too.

15. Push the hammer pivot pin out toward the right, and remove the hammer upward.

17. Remove the safety toward either side. If the detent ball was not previously removed, it can now be pushed downward into the safety tunnel and taken out.

18. Remove the large screw in the front of the fore-end, and slide the fore-end wood off toward the front.

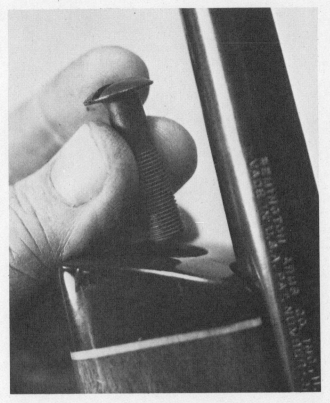

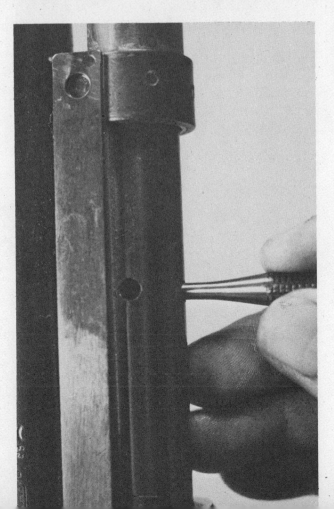

19. Insert a large drift punch through the holes in the action tube, and unscrew it counter-clockwise (front view). When the tube has cleared its threads, move it forward, into the action slide tube.

20. Move the barrel and action slide assembly forward out of the receiver. During this operation, take care that the ejection port cover is not damaged.

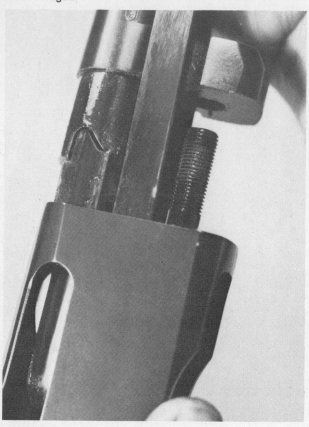

21. Move the slide assembly toward the rear, to clear the bolt from the barrel. Move the bolt assembly downward, out of the rear arch of the slide bars, tilt it to clear the bars, and remove it downward.

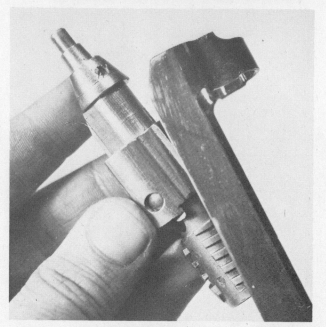

22. Position the rear end of the barrel at midpoint between the action slide bars, spread the bars just enough for clearance, and move them upward over the rear of the barrel. Remove the action slide assembly toward the front.

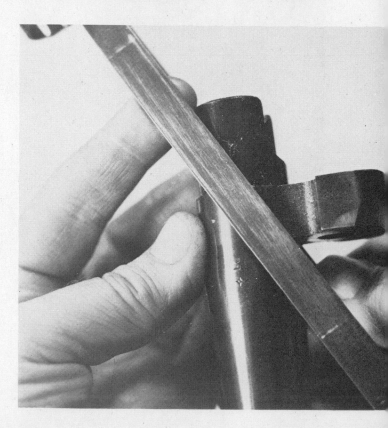

23. Insert a small screwdriver from the front to lift the small cam pin out of the bolt carrier, and remove it. Repeat the operation on the opposite side, lifting the larger cam pin out of the carrier, and remove it.

24. Remove the bolt from the carrier, toward the front.

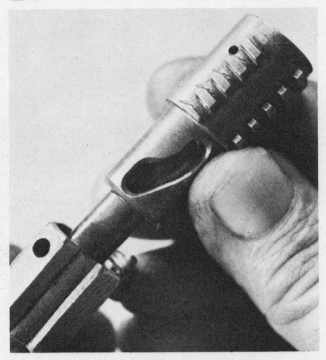

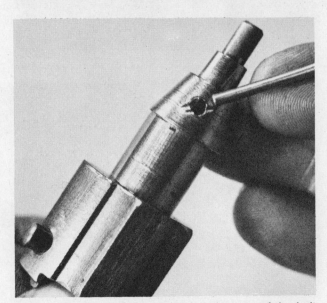

25. The firing pin is retained at the rear of the bolt carrier by a cross-pin, and is removed toward the rear. The bolt carrier tension spring can be removed from the front of the carrier.

26. The ejector is retained by a cross-pin near the front of the bolt, and is removed toward the front. **Caution:** *The ejector spring is under tension. Ease it out after removing the pin.*

27. The extractor is retained inside the bolt face recess by a small rivet, and should never be removed except for replacement of a broken part. If it must be taken out, the ejector must first be removed, then the rivet is driven inward with a small-diameter punch.

28. The buttstock is retained by a through-bolt from the rear, accessible by removing the buttplate. Use a B-Square stock tool or a long screwdriver to back out the bolt, and remove the stock toward the rear. If the stock is tight, bump the front of the comb with the heel of the hand to free it. Take care not to lose the bearing plate between the stock and receiver.

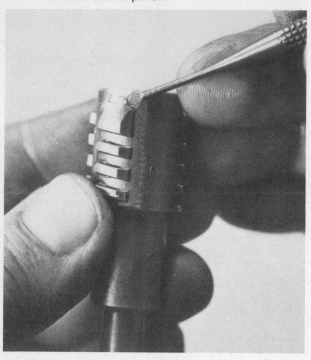

Reassembly Tips:

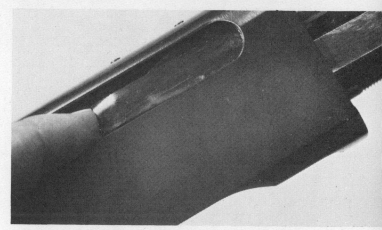

1. When replacing the ejection port cover, as the bolt and slide assembly are moved toward the rear, be sure the top edge of the cover enters the groove in the top of the receiver at the edge of the ejection port. The cover is easily broken.

2. When replacing the front cross-pin sleeve, note that the slot in its left tip must be positioned at the bottom, to engage the rear arm of the bolt latch spring.

3. When replacing the trigger, note that its left connector arm must be installed *above* the rear arm of the slide latch, as shown.

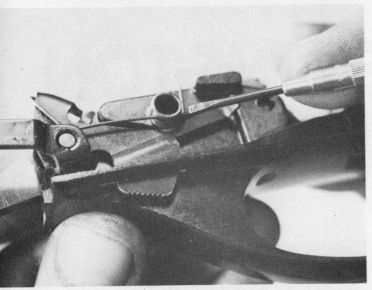

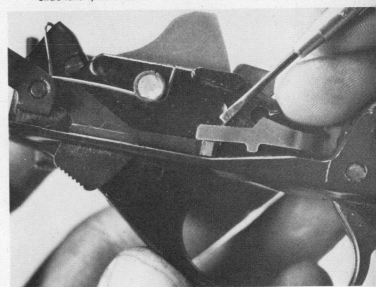

4. When replacing the trigger group in the receiver, remember to insert it forward of its position, then move it back to align with the cross-pins.

REMINGTON MODEL 788

Data:	Remington Model 788
Origin:	United States
Manufacturer:	Remington Arms Company Bridgeport, Connecticut
Cartridges:	222, 223, 22-250, 308, 243, 6mm Remington, and 44 Magnum
Magazine capacity:	4 rounds in 222, 3 in others
Over-all length:	41⅝ inches
Barrel length:	22 and 24 inches
Weight:	7 to 7½ pounds

A glance at the cartridges listed for the Model 788 may lead some to believe there's an error here, but the gun was actually offered for a short time in 44 Magnum chambering. The others listed are still available. For those who have the 44 Magnum version, it should be noted that their bolt is different, having a two-piece construction and a non-rotating bolt head. The Model 788 was introduced in 1967, and is still being offered by Remington.

Disassembly:

1. Remove the magazine. Open the bolt and move it toward the rear, while pushing the safety forward beyond its off-safe position. Remove the bolt from the rear of the receiver.

2. Insert a small-diameter drift punch into the tiny transverse hole in the bolt endpiece, being sure that it goes deep enough to enter the hole in the sriker head inside.

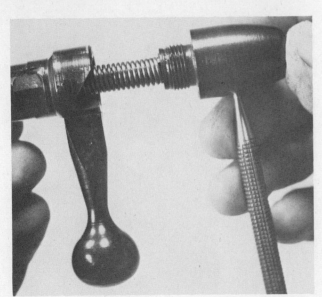

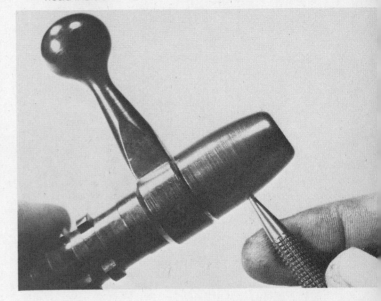

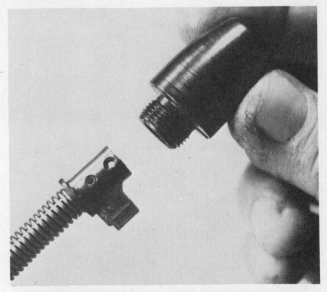

3. Leaving the drift punch in place, unscrew the bolt endpiece and striker assembly, removing it toward the rear.

4. Grip the heavy front portion of the striker firmly in a vise, and exert forward pressure on the endpiece while removing the drift punch from the hole. **Caution:** *The compressed spring is powerful, so keep a firm hold on the endpiece.* Slowly ease the endpiece off the rear of the striker assembly, and remove it toward the rear. The striker assembly can be taken apart by drifting out the retaining cross-pin in the striker head, but this is definitely not recommended in normal takedown.

5. Drifting out the cross-pin near the front of the bolt will release the ejector and its spring toward the front. **Caution:** *The spring is a strong one, so control the parts and ease them out.*

6. The extractor is retained inside the cartridge head recess in the bolt face by a tiny rivet, and in normal disassembly *its removal is not recommended,* as the extractor will almost invariably break. If removal of a broken extractor is necessary, drift out the rivet inward, using a small-diameter punch. Note that the ejector must be removed before this is done.

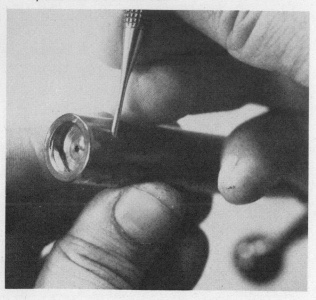

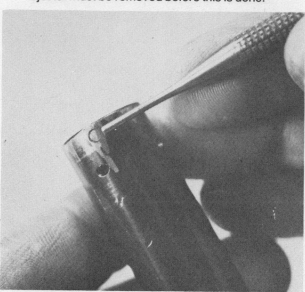

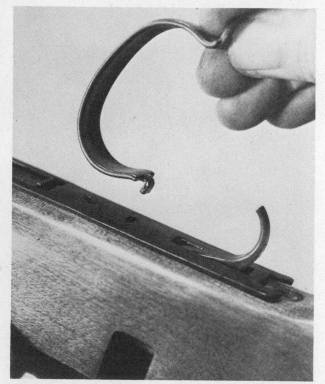

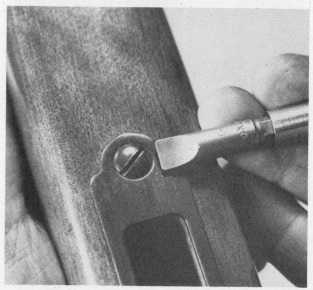

7. Remove the vertical screw at the rear of the trigger guard. Swing the guard downward and toward the front, and remove it.

8. Remove the large vertical screw on the underside just forward of the magazine opening, and separate the action from the stock.

9. The magazine guide bar and catch piece can be removed by backing out the vertical screw in its rear tail, on the underside of the receiver.

10. The trigger housing is retained by a single roll cross-pin at its top center. Use a roll pin punch to drift it out.

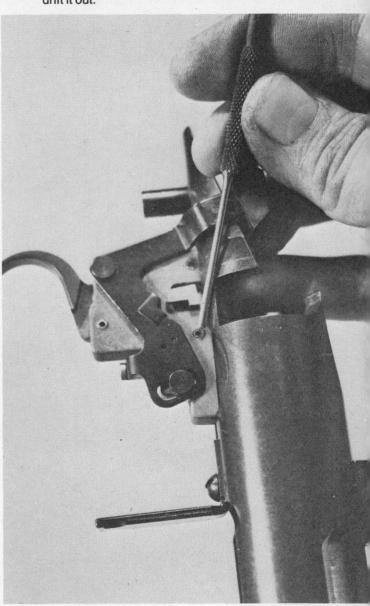

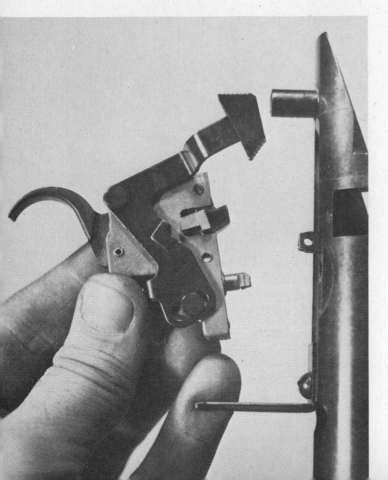

11. Remove the trigger housing downward.

12. Tipping the sear upward will allow removal of the combination sear and trigger spring.

13. Drift out the roll pin at the upper rear of the trigger housing, and remove the sear upward.

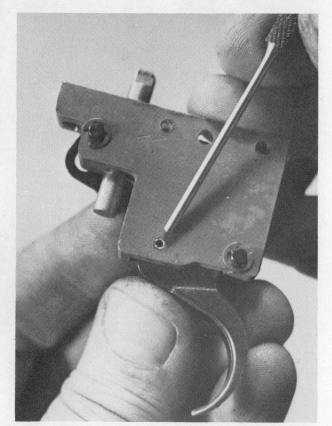

14. Drift out the roll cross-pin at the lower front of the trigger housing, and remove the trigger downward.

15. Remove the C-clip on the left side of the trigger housing at the front, and take out the forward safety guide pin toward the right. Hold the safety against the right side of the housing, as the positioning plunger and spring will tend to force it outward.

16. Remove the C-clip on the left side of the housing at the lower rear, and take out the safety pivot toward the right.

17. Restrain the bolt stop, and slowly ease the safety off toward the right.

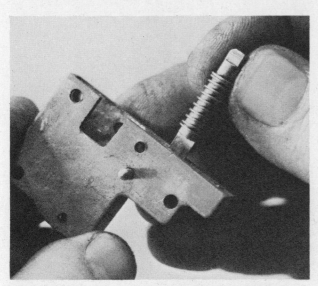

18. Remove the bolt stop and its spring from the top of the trigger housing.

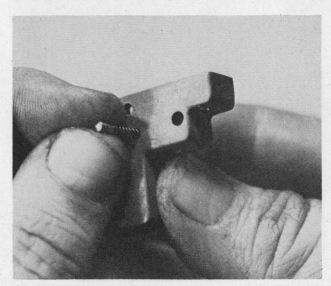

19. Remove the safety positioning plunger and its spring from the right side of the housing.

20. The housing tension screw, located in the front lip of the unit, is staked in place and should not be disturbed unless the housing is loose when re-mounted.

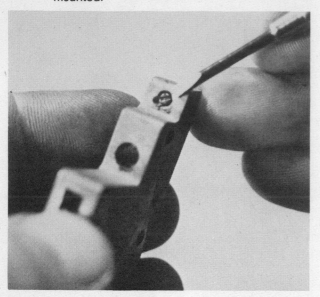

Reassembly Tips:

1. When the cocking piece is at the position shown, the drift punch can be re-inserted through the hole in the bolt endpiece to lock the striker assembly for re-placement in the bolt.

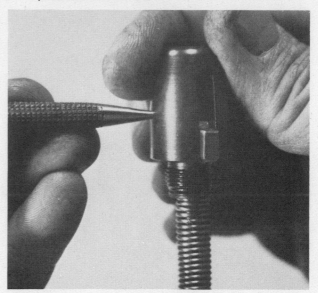

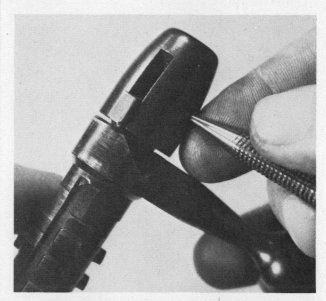

2. When turning the bolt endpiece and striker assembly back into the bolt, it should not be screwed down all the way. Stop it at the position shown, with the cocking lug aligned behind the full-cock detent notch, and withdraw the punch from the hole in the endpiece.

REMINGTON ROLLING BLOCK

Data: Remington Rolling Block

Origin: United States

Manufacturer: Remington Arms Company, Ilion, New York, Springfield Armory, and armories in several foreign countries

Cartridges: 50 U.S., 45 Danish, 43 Spanish, 7×57, many others

Over-all length: 46 inches (Carbine, 35⅝ inches)

Barrel length: 30 inches (Carbine, 20½ inches)

Weight: 8½ pounds (Carbine, 7 pounds)

Note: Weights and measurements are for the 7mm model of 1897-1902, used mainly in Central and South America

In 1866, Joseph Rider re-designed the Remington-Geiger action, and the Rolling Block was born. In the years between 1870 and 1900, this gun became the official military arm of a large number of countries, and was also used by the U.S. Navy. Its ingenious "rolling" breech-block made the action a very strong one, and its simplicity made it ideal for military use. The era of the bolt action repeater ended its military career, but Remington made it as a sporting rifle up to 1933.

Disassembly:

1. Back out the vertical screw at the rear of the upper tang, and remove the buttstock toward the rear. If the stock is very tight, bump the front of the comb with the heel of the hand to start it.

2. If the gun is equipped with a saddle ring, back out the ring bar screw, and swing the bar upward. Remove the ring. The bar is threaded into the side of the receiver, and is not removed at this time.

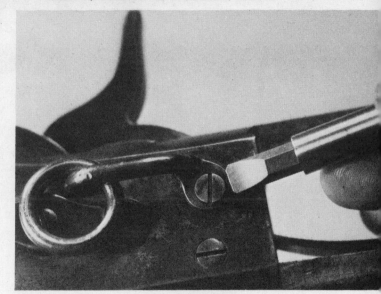

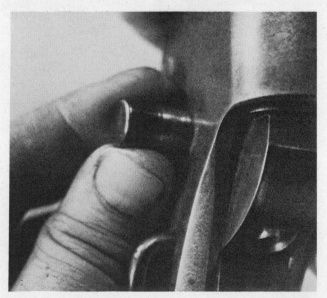

3. Remove the screw at the center of the lock plate, located between the two large pins on the left side of the receiver (Note: Remington called the lock plate the "button"). Take off the lock plate toward the left.

4. Cock the hammer, and push out the breechblock pivot pin toward the left. If the pin is tight, use a non-marring nylon or brass drift punch to start it.

5. Remove the small screw on the left side of the receiver, just below the breechblock pivot hole.

6. Remove the breechblock assembly, including the ejector, upward and toward the rear.

7. The ejector is easily detached from the left side of the breechblock.

8. Drifting out the lower cross-pin in the breechblock will allow the firing pin retractor to be taken out downward, and removal of the upper cross-pin will free the firing pin, which is taken out toward the rear.

9. Restrain the hammer, pull the trigger, and ease the hammer down beyond its normal full forward position. Push out the hammer pivot toward the left.

10. Remove the hammer upward.

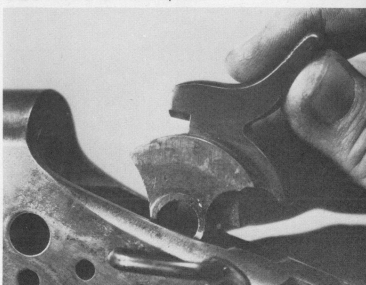

11. If the gun has a saddle ring bar, it can now be unscrewed from the left side of the receiver and taken off. When unscrewing it, lift its free end slightly during the first few turns, to avoid marring the receiver.

12. Remove the cross-screw at the lower front of the receiver.

13. Remove the cross-screw at the lower rear of the receiver.

14. Remove the trigger guard assembly downward and toward the rear.

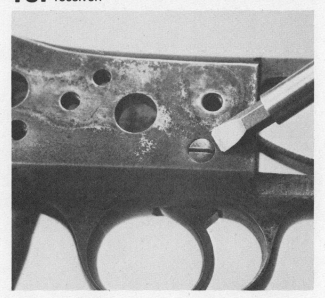

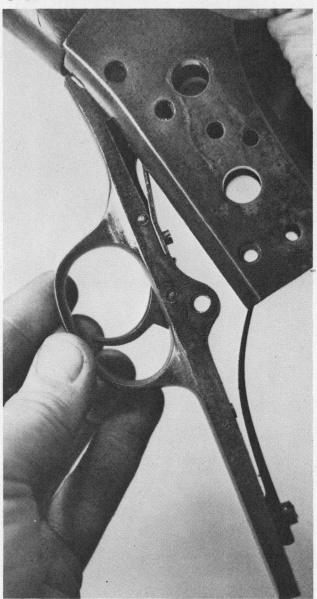

15. Remove the hammer spring screw, and take off the hammer spring upward.

16. Remove the trigger spring screw, and take out the trigger spring upward.

17. Drift out the trigger cross-pin, and remove the trigger upward.

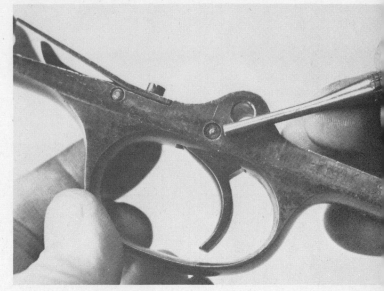

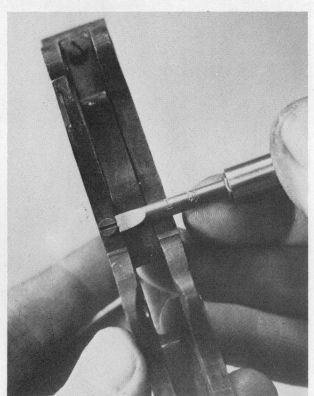

18. Remove the ejector spring screw, and take off the ejector spring upward.

19. Drift out the cross-pin at the front of the guard, and remove the breechblock locking lever upward. **Caution:** *This pin is very near the upper edge of the guard frame, so take care that the edge is not broken during removal.*

20. Remove the vertical screw at the front of the guard unit, and take out the locking lever spring upward.

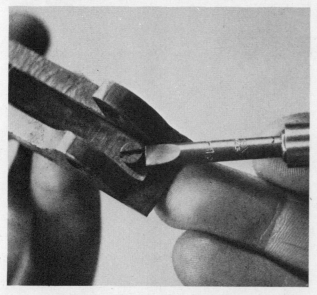

21. If the gun is a full-length rifle, there will be three barrel bands to be removed. On the carbine, as shown, remove the single band by depressing its spring latch and sliding it off toward the front. The fore-end wood can now be taken off downward.

22. Before the upper handguard wood can be removed, the rear sight must be taken off by backing out its two screws, at the front and rear of the sight base.

Reassembly Tips:

1. After the hammer is installed on its pivot in the receiver, insert a tool from the rear to depress the front of the hammer spring, to insure that the tip of the spring engages the spring lobe on the rear of the hammer.

2. When replacing the breechblock assembly in the receiver, you must exert downward pressure on the assembly while inserting the pivot pin, to slightly compress the lock lever and the ejector spring.

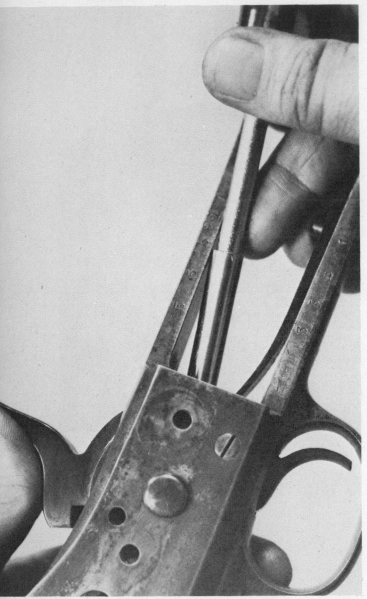

RUGER 44 CARBINE

Data:	Ruger 44 Carbine
Origin:	United States
Manufacturer:	Sturm, Ruger & Company Southport, Connecticut
Cartridge:	44 Magnum
Magazine capacity:	4 rounds
Over-all length:	36¾ inches
Barrel length:	18½ inches
Weight:	5¾ pounds

When the Ruger 44 Autoloading Carbine arrived in 1961, it was the first rifle chambered for this round, and is still the only semi-auto regularly available in this chambering. It has gained much popularity as a close-range gun for medium game, and the ballistics of its cartridge are comparable to the old 30-30. Like all of Bill Ruger's creations, it is an engineering masterpiece. It is not unnecessarily complicated, but an inter-dependency of certain parts makes takedown and reassembly an endeavor best left to the professional.

Disassembly:

1. Pull back the operating handle to lock the bolt open. Remove the cross-screw at the bottom of the barrel band, and take off the band toward the front.

2. Lift the action at the front, and disengage its rear hook from the recoil block in the stock. Take out the action upward and toward the front.

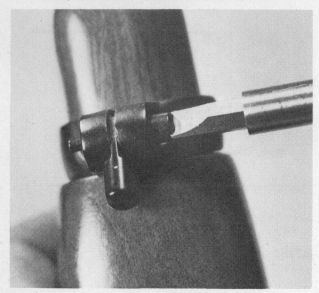

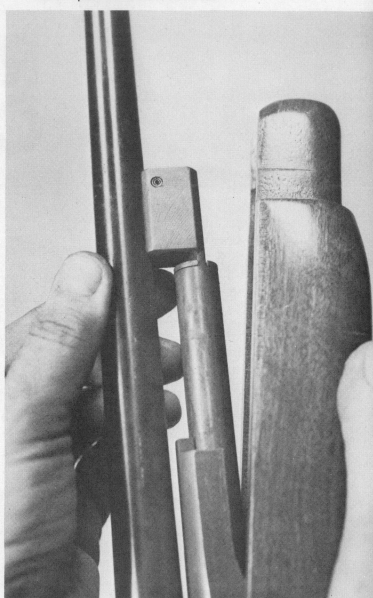

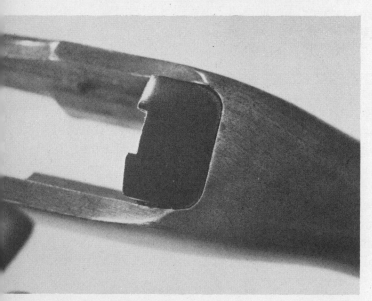

3. If necessary, the recoil block can be removed by taking off the buttplate and backing out the through-bolt which enters the block from the rear. The block is then removed forward and upward.

4. Push the lifter latch, and ease the bolt to closed position. Drift out the cross-pin at the rear of the receiver.

5. Move the trigger housing toward the rear, and take it off downward.

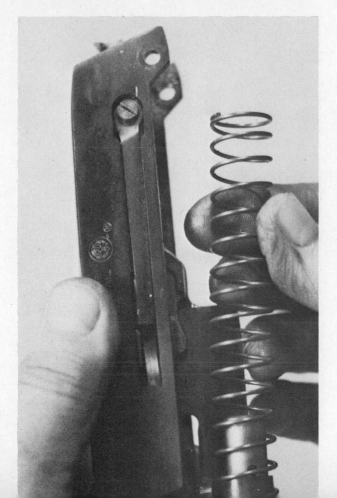

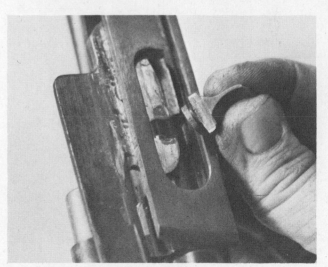

7. Remove the bolt handle from its slot in the action slide, and take it off toward the right.

6. With the gun inverted, grip the rear of the recoil spring firmly, and lift the action slide away from the bottom of the receiver. As soon as the rear end of the spring has cleared the edge of the receiver, slowly release the spring and remove it toward the rear.

8. Remove the action slide and magazine tube together from the bottom of the receiver. Separate the magazine tube from the action slide.

9. Drifting out the roll pin at the front of the magazine tube will allow removal of the tube endpiece, magazine spring, and follower. **Caution:** *The spring is under tension, so control the endpiece and ease it out.*

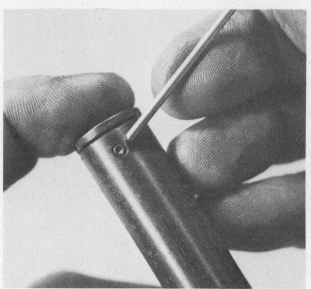

10. Remove the screw at the left rear of the receiver, and take off the ejector toward the left.

11. Insert a finger through the ejection port to turn the bolt and free its locking lugs, then move it toward the rear about half-way. Lift the bolt out of the underside of the receiver.

12. The gas piston is usually easy to remove from the rear of the gas cylinder. If it is tight because of powder residue, tap the rear flange of the cylinder with a plastic hammer to nudge it out.

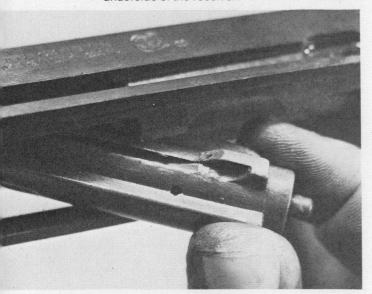

13. The piston block plug at the front of the gas cylinder is retained by two concentric roll pins, and is removed toward the front. In normal takedown, it is best left in place.

14. The firing pin is retained in the bolt by a pin at the rear, and the firing pin and its return spring are taken out toward the rear.

15. The extractor is retained by a vertcial pin at the front of the bolt, and this pin must be driven out upward. The extractor and its coil spring are then removed toward the right.

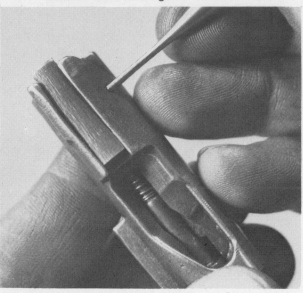

16. Restrain the hammer, pull the trigger, and ease the hammer down to the fired position. Unhook the outer arms of the hammer spring, on each side of the housing, from the grooved ends of the hammer pivot pin, partially relieving the tension of the springs. **Caution:** *Use pliers to disengage the springs, as they are under heavy tension.*

17. When the spring arms are turned downward, the hammer spring pin can be pushed out and removed. After removal of the pin the springs will be loose, but they are not taken out at this time.

18. Push out the hammer pivot pin toward either side.

19. Remove the hammer upward.

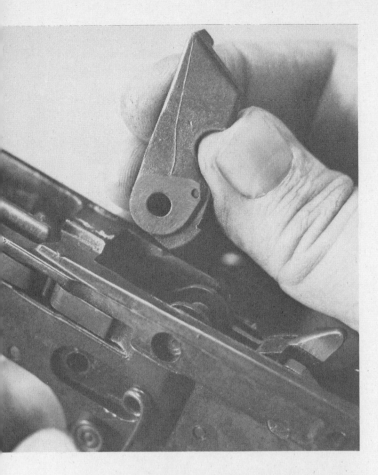

20. 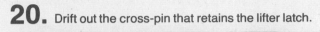 Drift out the cross-pin that retains the lifter latch.

21. Raise the lifter at the front, and take out the lifter latch downward. The plunger and spring are easily detached from the rear of the lifter latch.

22. Move the front of the lifter back to its lowered position to relieve tension on the cam spring, and push out the lifter cam pin toward the left.

23. Insert an angled drift punch through the lifter cam pin hole, and lever the lifter cam slightly toward the rear. Raise the front of the lifter, and remove the cam and its spring upward and toward the front.

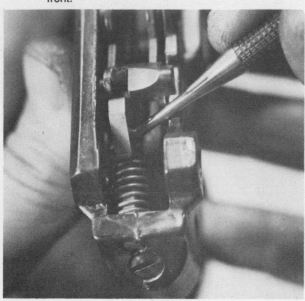

24. Insert a small screwdriver on the left side at the rear tip of the carrier, and push the lifter dog pin out toward the right until it can be grasped with pliers and pulled out. Remove the lifter dog upward.

25. Squeeze the rear arms of the carrier (lifter) together, to move the side studs from their holes in the sides of the housing, and remove it upward and toward the rear.

26. Push out the trigger pin, and move the twin hammer springs out to each side to clear the trigger and sear assembly.

27. Remove the trigger, sear, and disconnector assembly upward, and remove the sear spring from its well in the housing.

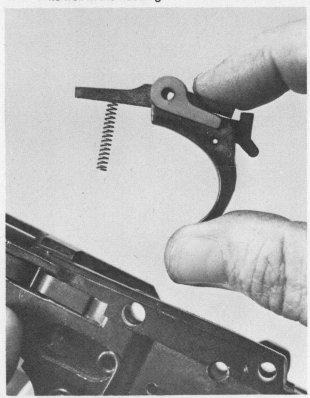

28. Remove the trigger plunger and spring from its hole at the rear of the trigger guard.

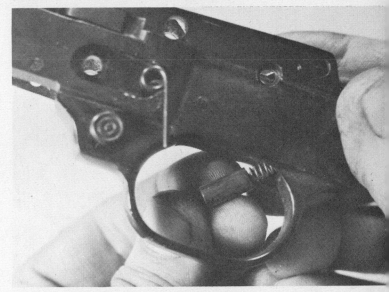

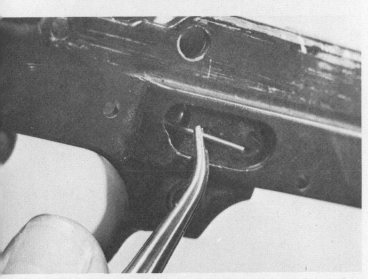

29. Move the hammer springs inward, one at a time, tip the outer arms outward, and push the springs into the interior of the trigger housing for removal.

30. Grip the safety with smooth-jawed parallel pliers, and give it one-quarter turn clockwise (right side view). Remove the safety toward the left. **Caution:** *The safety plunger and spring will be released as the safety clears, so insert a screwdriver into the housing to restrain them.*

31. The flat cartridge stop spring is retained on the left side of the trigger housing by a vertical pin which is in a blind hole. Use a small screwdriver to nudge it upward until it can be grasped with pliers and taken out. The flat spring is then removed toward the left.

32. After the flat spring is removed, take out the rearmost of the two coil springs from its hole in the trigger housing.

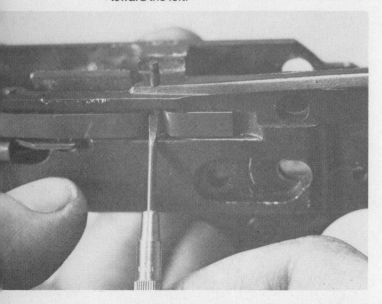

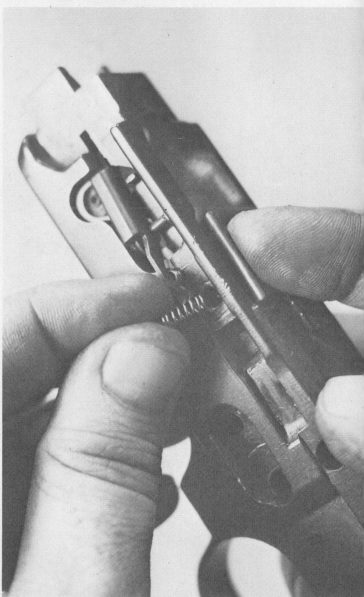

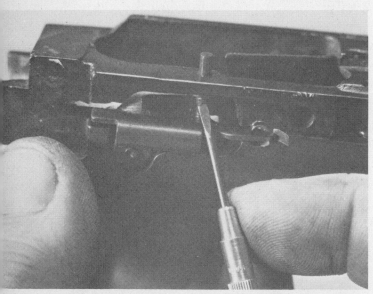

33. The cartridge stop and flapper pivot pin is also in a blind hole, and is removed in the same way as the previous one. Note that the cartridge stop spring will be released when the pin is out, so control it.

Reassembly Tips:

34. Remove the cartridge stop and its spring toward the left, and move the flapper inward and take it out toward the top of the housing.

1. When replacing the cartridge stop system, note that the cartridge stop spring and the flapper spring are of unequal length. Remember that the shorter spring goes at the front, under the tail of the cartridge stop.

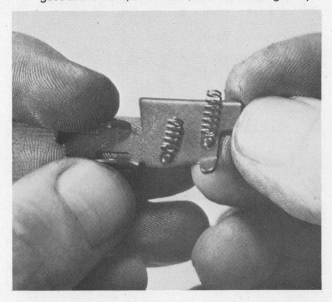

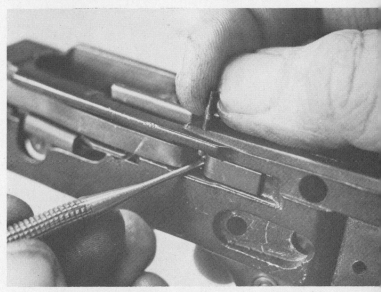

2. When replacing the flat cartridge stop spring, it is necessary to lay the housing on its right side on a firm surface, and use a small drift punch to depress the spring at its pin dip to allow passage of the pin.

3. It is possible to install the sear/trigger/disconnector system by just holding them in place, but the use of a slave pin to hold the parts together will make it much easier. Be sure the lower end of the sear spring enters its hole inside of the trigger housing, and be sure the rear tail of the disconnector goes in front of the trigger spring plunger at the rear.

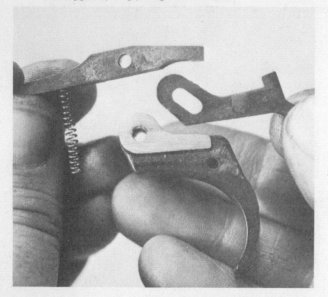

4. When replacing the hammer springs, they must be reinserted from inside the trigger group. When the long arm of the spring is protruding to the outside, insert a drift punch into the center of the spring, and tilt the drift toward the front of the housing, levering the spring into its hole.

5. Installing the hammer is perhaps the most difficult of reassembly operations. Be sure the short inner arms of both hammer springs engage the underside of the small roller at the lower rear of the hammer. Push the hammer straight downward, and insert a drift punch through the hammer pivot hole to hold it in place for insertion of the cross-pin. Be sure the spring ends are not allowed to slip from beneath the roller during installation of the pin. Remember to replace the spring cross-pin, and re-hook the spring arms onto the hammer pivot pin.

6. When replacing the magazine tube, note that the slot in the tube endpiece of offset, and must fit onto the flange at the rear of the gas piston housing. The larger area of the endpiece goes toward the barrel, as shown.

7. When replacing the magazine tube and recoil spring assembly, note that at the rear the spring must bear against the receiver, and must not extend into the recess for the rear tip of the magazine tube, as shown.

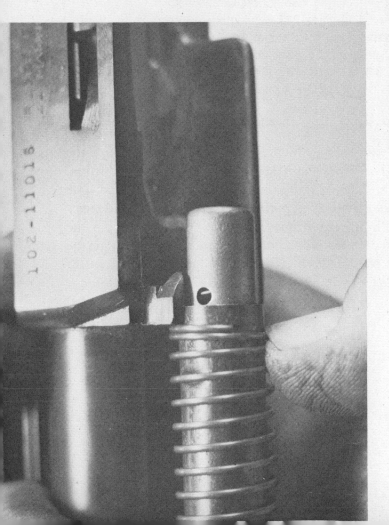

8. When properly assembled, the spring and tube will be as shown.

RUGER MINI-14

Data:	Ruger Mini-14
Origin:	United States
Manufacturer:	Sturm, Ruger & Company Southport, Connecticut
Cartridge:	223 Remington (5.56mm)
Magazine capacity:	5 rounds
Over-all length:	37¼ inches
Barrel length:	18½ inches
Weight:	6.4 pounds

While externally it may appear to be a miniature of the U.S. M-14 rifle, the Mini-14 is all Ruger on the inside. Introduced in 1973, this neat little carbine has gained wide acceptance both as a sporting gun and in police and guard applications. There has been one small change in the original design—a bolt hold-open button was added on the top left side of the receiver, and all guns of more recent manufacture will have this feature.

Disassembly:

1. Remove the magazine, and cycle the action to cock the internal hammer. Push the safety back to the on-safe position, and insert a non-marring tool through the hole at the rear of the trigger guard to spring the guard downward at the rear. Swing the guard toward the front until it stops.

2. Remove the trigger housing downward.

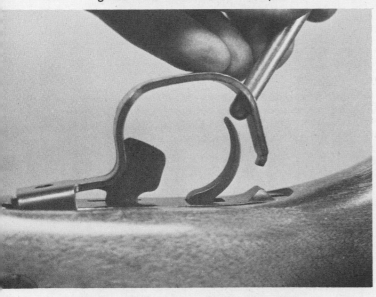

3. Tip the rear of the action upward out of the stock, and remove it toward the front.

4. Grasp the recoil spring firmly at the rear, where it joins the receiver, and lift the tip of the guide out of its hole in the front of the receiver. **Caution:** *This is a strong spring, so keep it under control.* Tilt the spring and guide upward, slowly release the tension, and remove the spring and guide toward the rear.

5. Move the slide assembly toward the rear until its rear lug aligns with the exit cut in the slide track, and move the operating handle upward and toward the right. Remove the slide assembly.

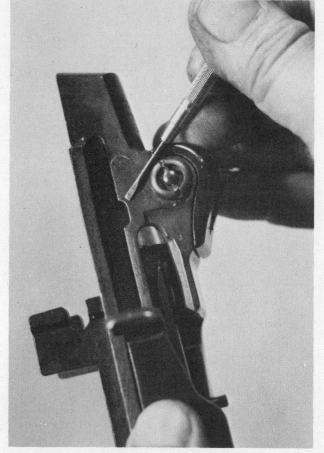

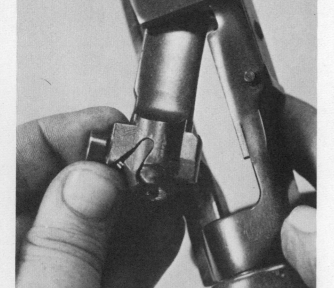

6. Move the bolt forward to the position shown, and remove it upward and toward the right. The bolt must be turned to align the underlug of the firing pin with the exit cut in the bottom of the bolt track.

7. In normal takedown, the gas block assembly should not be removed. If it is necessary, use an Allen wrench to remove the four vertical screws, separating the upper and lower sections of the gas block. The gas port bushing will be freed with removal of the lower block, so take care that it isn't lost.

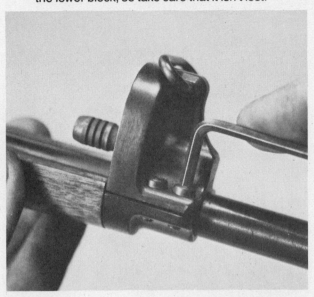

8. Slide the bolt hold-open cover downward out of its slots in the receiver and remove it.

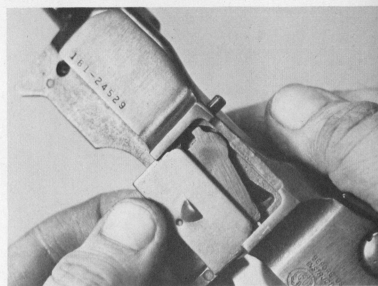

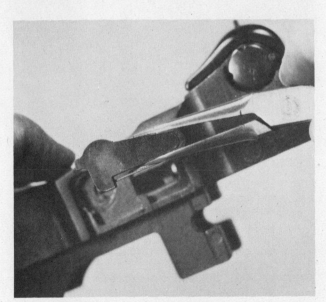

9. Depress the bolt latch plunger on top of the left receiver rail, and lift the bolt lock out of its recess toward the left. **Caution:** *The bolt latch retains the plunger, so control the plunger and ease it out upward, along with its spring.*

10. The front magazine catch, located in the front of the receiver below the barrel, is retained by a roll cross-pin, accessible through holes on each side. Drift out the cross-pin, and remove the catch toward the front.

11. Insert a small screwdriver beside the extractor plunger, and turn and tip the screwdriver to depress the plunger. Move the extractor upward out of its recess. **Caution:** *As the extractor post clears the ejector, it will be released, so restrain the ejector and ease it out toward the front. Also, take care to keep the extractor plunger under control, and ease it out.* Removal of the extractor will also free the firing pin to be taken out toward the rear.

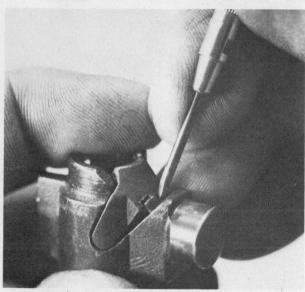

12. Close and latch the trigger guard, and insert a piece of rod or a drift punch through the hole in the rear tip of the hammer spring guide.

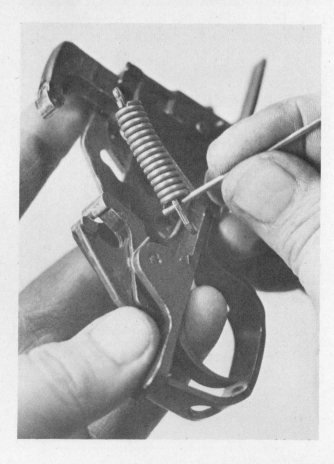

13. Restrain the hammer, move the safety to the off-safe position, and pull the trigger to release the hammer. The rod will trap the hammer spring on the guide. Tip the front of the guide upward, out of its recess at the rear of the hammer, and remove the guide assembly toward the right. If the spring is to be taken off the guide, proceed with care, as the spring is fully compressed.

14. Push out the hammer pivot, and remove the hammer upward and toward the right.

15. Move the safety back to the on-safe position, and take off the trigger guard downward and toward the rear.

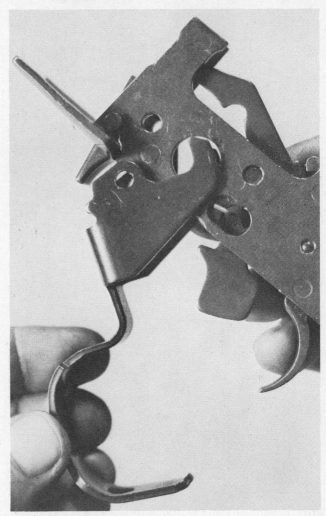

16. Drift out the safety spring pin toward the left, ease the spring tension slowly, and move the spring toward the rear, unhooking it from the safety. Remove the spring toward the right rear.

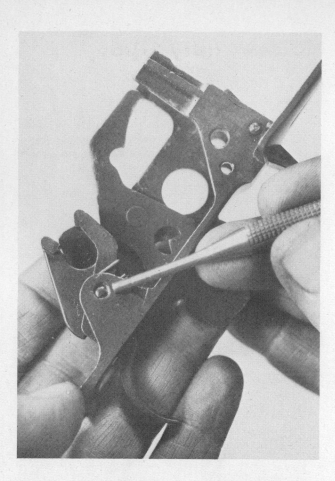

17. Restrain the trigger and sear assembly, and drift out the trigger cross-pin.

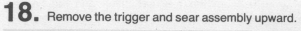

18. Remove the trigger and sear assembly upward.

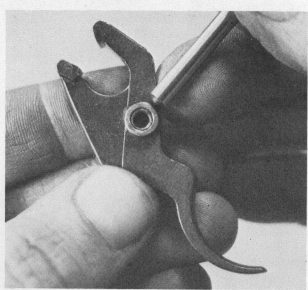

19. The trigger spring is easily detached from the trigger, and the pivot bushing can be drifted out to free the secondary sear and its coil spring from the top of the trigger. **Caution:** *Use a roll-pin punch to avoid damaging the bushing, and take care to restrain the sear against the tension of its spring.*

20. Tip the upper portion of the safety catch toward the right, moving is pivot stud out of its hole in the trigger housing, and remove the safety upward.

21. The main magazine catch is retained by a cross-pin at the front of the trigger housing, and the pin must be drifted out toward the left. **Caution:** *The strong magazine catch spring will also be released when the pin is removed, so insert a shop cloth into the housing behind the spring to catch it. This spring is rather difficult to re-install, so if removal is not necessary for repair, the catch is best left in place.*

Reassembly Tips:

1. When installing the trigger and sear assembly, tilt the assembly forward, and be sure the front hooks of the trigger spring engage the top of the cross-piece in the housing. Push the assembly downward and toward the rear until the cross-pin can be inserted.

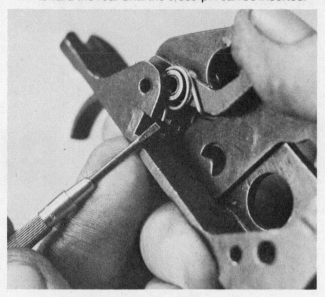

When replacing the safety spring, be sure that its front arm goes on the right side of the rear arm of the magazine catch spring. Otherwise, the safety spring pin cannot be fully inserted.

RUGER NO.1

Data:	Ruger No. 1
Origin:	United States
Manufacturer:	Sturm, Ruger & Company
	Southport, Connecticut
Cartridges:	Most popular calibers from 22-250 to 458
Over-all length:	42 inches
Barrel lengths:	22, 24 and 26 inches
Weight:	8 pounds

In 1967, Bill Ruger re-created the classic single-shot rifle, and over the past thirteen years it has proved to be an outstanding success. The action and some other features of the gun have some relationship to the old Fraser and Farquharson rifles from England, but the mechanism is pure Ruger, and superior to any other gun of this type, before or since. Also, in contrast to the older guns of this type, the takedown and reassembly operations are not difficult.

Disassembly:

1. Remove the angled screw on the underside of the fore-end and take off the fore-end forward and downward.

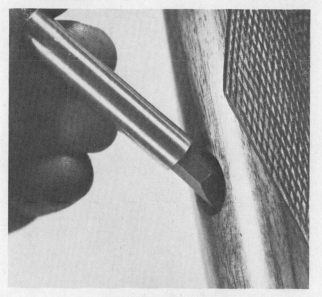

2. Remove the fore-end takedown nut, and set it aside to prevent loss.

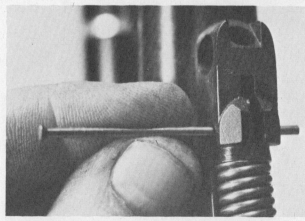

3. Cycle the action to cock the hammer, and insert a small piece of rod through the transverse hole in the front tip of the hammer spring strut. Pull the trigger to release the hammer.

4. Move the hammer spring assembly slightly toward the rear, tip the front of the assembly downward, and remove it toward the front. If the assembly is to be taken apart, proceed with caution, as the spring is compressed.

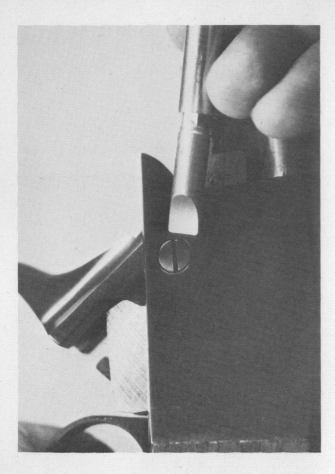

5. Remove the cap screw on the lever pivot, and push out the pivot toward the opposite side. The action should be opened while this is done. If the screw is very tight, the lever pivot head has a screw slot, and it can be held with another screwdriver.

6. Remove the hammer downward.

7. Push the breechblock back upward, close the lever, then open the lever about half way, and remove the lever and breechblock assembly downward out of the receiver as a unit.

8. Detach the breechblock from the lever arm, and remove the ejector roller from the left side of the breechblock.

9. Holding the breechblock with its left side downward, reach into the underside of the block and work the hammer transfer block back and forth until its pivot pin protrudes from the left side enough to be caught with a fingernail or small screwdriver and pulled out. The pin has a cannelure at its left tip for this purpose.

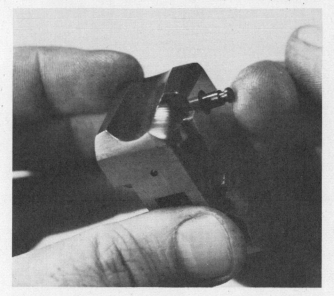

10. Remove the hammer transfer block from the bottom of the breechblock. The firing pin and its return spring can now be taken out from inside the breechblock.

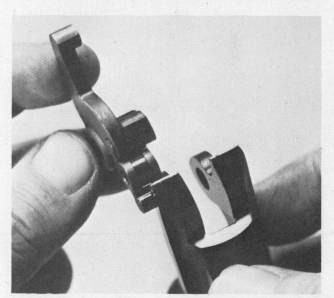

11. The breechblock arm and the lever links are easily separated from each other. Note that the links are joined by a roll pin, and this should be left in place unless removal is necessary for repair.

12. Backing out the cross-screw in the tail of the lever will allow removal of the lever latch and its spring.

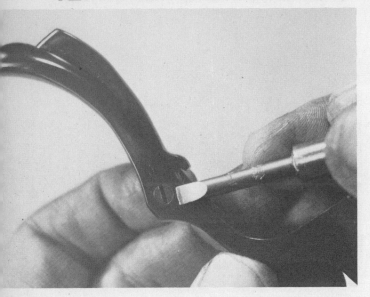

13. Remove the ejector downard, and take care not to lose the plunger and spring mounted in its side.

14. The plunger and spring are easily removed from the side of the ejector.

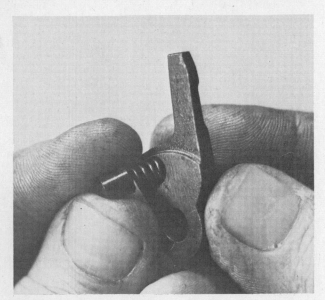

15. Tip the ejector lever (ejector cam) downward, and take off its spring and guide assembly downward. Note that the guide is two separate parts.

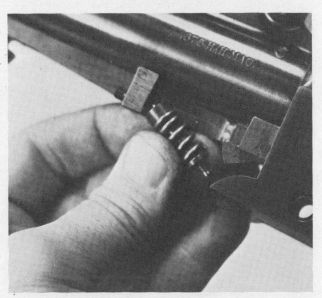

16. Drifting out its pivot pin will allow removal of the ejector cam lever toward the front.

17. The buttstock is retained by a through-bolt from the rear. Take off the buttplate, and use a B-square stock tool or a large screwdriver to back out the stock bolt. Remove the stock toward the rear. If it is very tight, bump the front of the comb with the heel of the hand to start it.

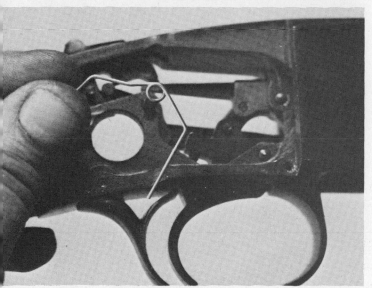

18. Unhook the upper arm of the safety positioning spring from its stud on the safety, and remove the spring from its mounting post toward the right.

19. Removal of the safety button requires the drifting out of two roll pins in its underlug, just below the upper tang.

20. Drifting out this post from the opposite side (from right to left) will release the safety arm and safety bar as a unit to be moved toward the rear and taken out toward the side. This is the same post that is the mounting stud for the safety positioning spring.

21. The trigger guard is retained by two roll pins at the front and rear, crossing the lower tang of the receiver. When these are drifted out, the guard is removed downward.

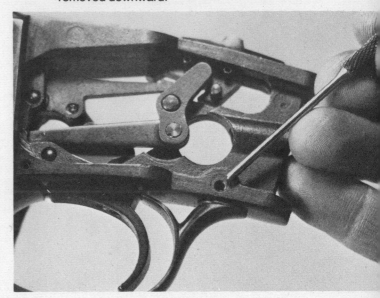

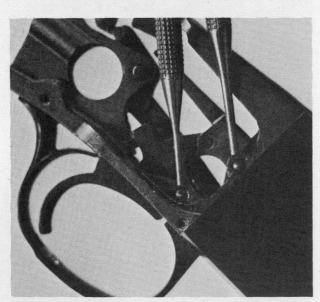

22. The trigger and sear are retained by cross-pins, and are joined by a link. After the pins are removed, the trigger and sear are moved slightly toward the rear, then are taken out downward, with their attendant springs.

Reassembly Tips:

1. This view of the right side of the receiver with the stock removed shows the internal parts in their proper order. The safety is shown in the on-safe position.

2. This view of the left side of the receiver shows the safety in the off-safe position.

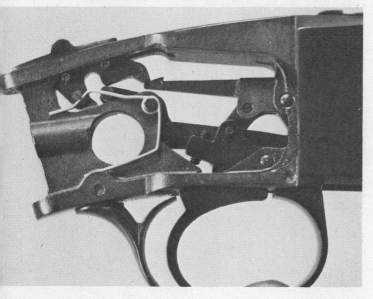

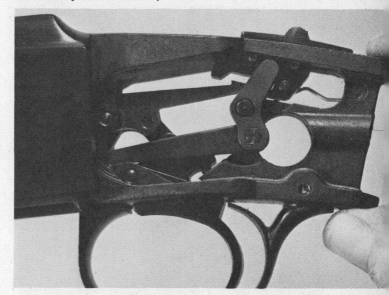

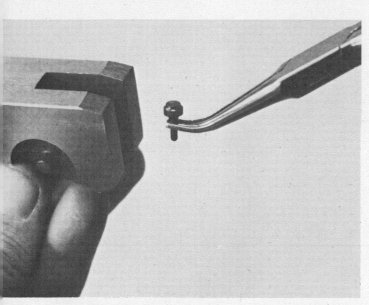

3. After the firing pin spring is in place inside the breechblock, grip the firing pin with forceps or very slim pliers, and set the firing pin point into the spring.

4. When replacing the hammer transfer block, note that the concave area in its lower extension goes toward the rear.

5. When replacing the hammer spring assembly, note that the down-turned neck at the rear of the strut goes in that position—downward.

RUGER MODEL 77

Data:	Ruger Model 77
Origin:	United States
Manufacturer:	Sturm, Ruger & Company Southport, Connecticut
Cartridges:	Most popular calibers from 22-250 to 458
Magazine capacity:	3 to 5 rounds
Over-all length:	42 to 44 inches
Barrel length:	22 to 26 inches
Weight:	6¾ pounds (Standard)

With some elements of the classic Mauser/Springfield rifle, in 1968 Bill Ruger created a gun that includes the best points of the old and new. Internally, the Model 77 is all modern, with several Ruger innovations, such as the angled front action mounting screw which pulls the action not only down in the stock, but also back, snugging the recoil lug against the interior of the stock. The firing mechanism is uncomplicated, and takedown and reassembly are not difficult.

Disassembly:

1. Open the bolt and move it to the rear, while holding the bolt stop pulled out toward the left. Remove the bolt from the rear of the receiver.

2. Insert a small piece of rod (or a drift punch) at the lower rear of the cocking piece, into the hole provided. This will lock the striker in rear position. Unscrew the striker assembly counter-clockwise (rear view).

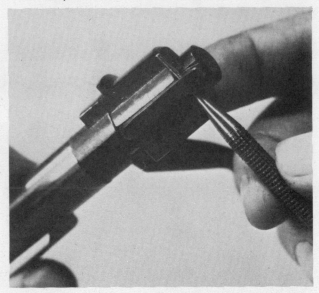

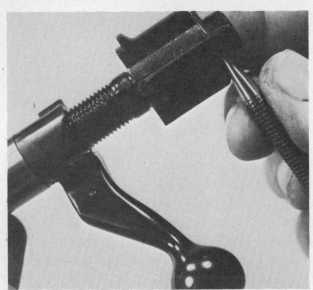

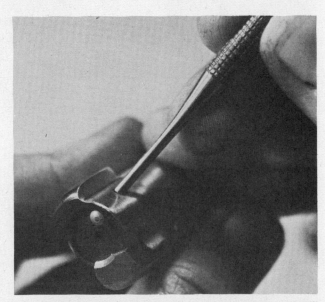

3. Remove the striker assembly from the rear of the bolt. It is possible to grip the front of the striker in a vise and push the bolt endpiece forward to expose a cross-pin in the cocking piece, and drifting out this pin would release the parts of the striker assembly. There is, however, no reasonably easy way to do this without special tools, and the factory cautions against taking this assembly apart.

4. Drifting out the vertical pin at the front of the bolt will release the ejector and its spring toward the front. **Caution:** *The spring is compressed, so restrain the ejector and ease it out.*

5. Turn the extractor counter-clockwise (rear view) until it is aligned with the base of the bolt handle, then use the Brownells extractor pliers or a small screwdriver blade to lift the front underlug of the extractor out of its groove at the front of the bolt, and push the extractor off the flanges of the mounting ring toward the front.

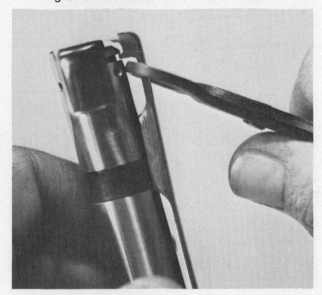

6. Open the magazine floorplate, and slide the magazine spring out of its slots. The follower can be removed from the spring in the same way.

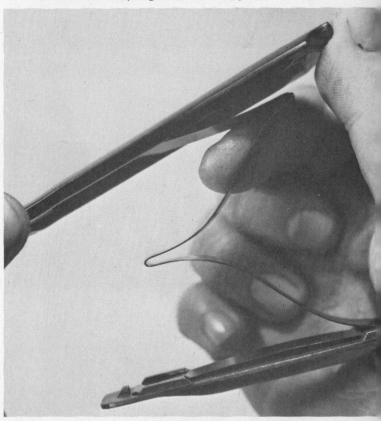

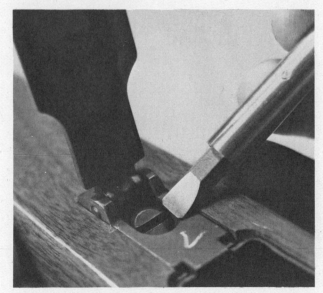

7. Remove the large angled screw inside the front of the magazine floorplate base.

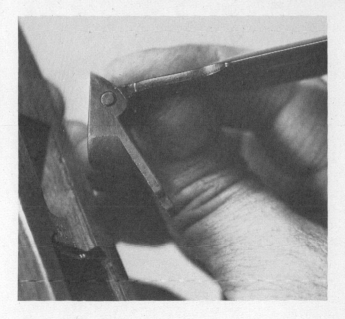

8. Remove the magazine floorplate and its base downward. Pushing out the hinge pin will allow separation of the floorplate and its base.

9. Remove the vertical screw at the front of the trigger guard. Remove the vertical screw at the rear of the trigger guard, and take off the trigger guard downward. Separate the action from the stock.

10. Drifting out the cross-pin in the front of the trigger guard will allow removal of the magazine floorplate latch and its spring.

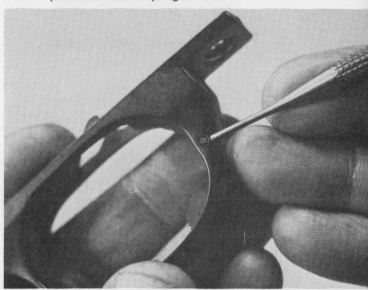

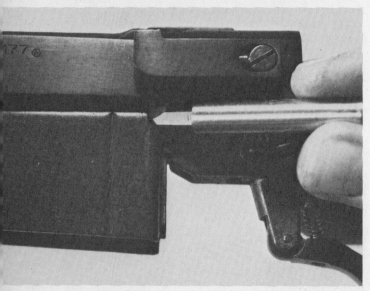

11. The magazine box is a press fit in its recess in the bottom of the receiver. Insert a tool in the openings on each side at the upper rear of the box, and gently pry it away from the receiver.

12. The bolt stop is removed by backing out its mounting screw toward the left.

13. As the screw is backed out, the bolt stop plunger will drop from the edge of the screw head to the internal bushing, and the stud screw is then easily removed.

14. Drifting out the vertical roll pin at the front of the bolt stop will allow removal of the spring and plunger toward the front, and the bushing from the rear opening.

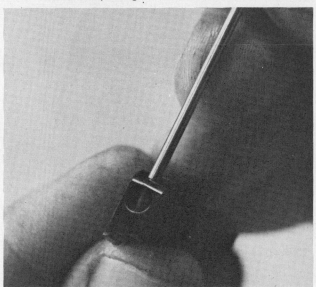

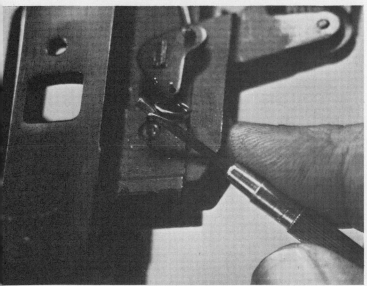

15. With the safety in the on-safe position, use a small screwdriver to lift the front arm of the safety positioning spring out of the center of the trigger housing roll pin. When it is clear, swing it downward, and unhook it from the hole in the edge of the safety shaft plate.

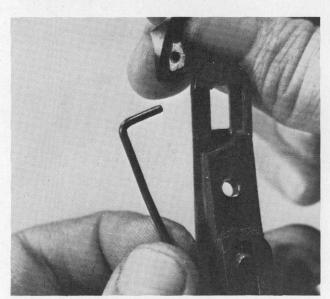

16. Move the rear tip of the safety link out of its cross-hole in the underside of the safety button, and unhook its forward end from the safety plate. The safety button can now be removed.

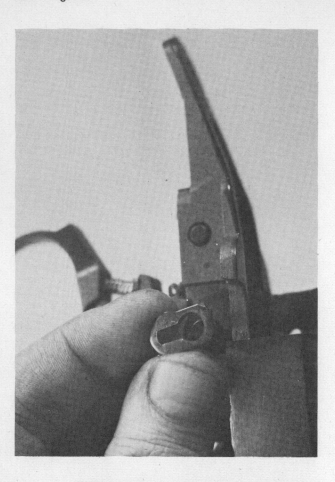

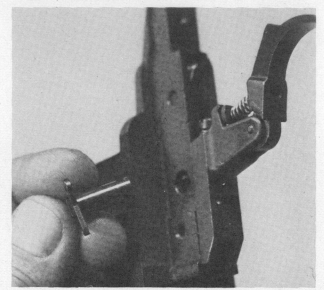

17. After the link rod is removed, push the safety plate toward the right, moving the right tip of its shaft slightly out of the right side of the housing. The safety bolt lock can then be slid off the shaft downward, then removed toward the right.

18. Remove the safety shaft and and its attached plate toward the left.

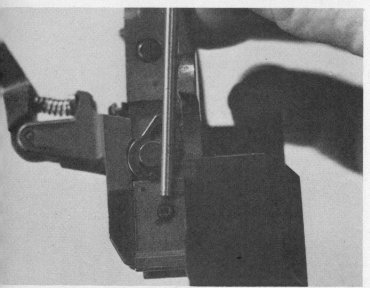

19. Drift out the trigger housing cross-pin toward the left, using a roll pin punch. It is important that the ends of this pin are not deformed, as the safety positioning spring must be remounted inside the pin.

20. Remove the trigger housing downward.

21. Move the trigger spring base out of its seat at the rear of the housing, and remove the spring toward the rear. **Caution:** *The spring is under tension.*

22. Pushing out the trigger pin will release the trigger from the housing. The trigger adjustment screws should not be disturbed.

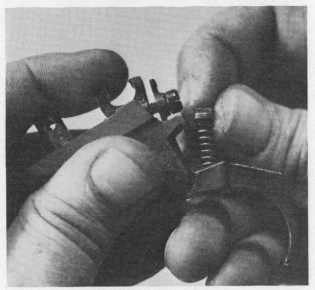

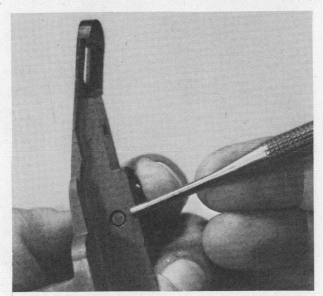

23. Restrain the sear against its spring tension, and push out the sear pin toward the right side. Remove the sear and its spring downward.

Reassembly Tips:

1. When replacing the safety shaft, the trigger must be pulled to clear the shaft tunnel for insertion.

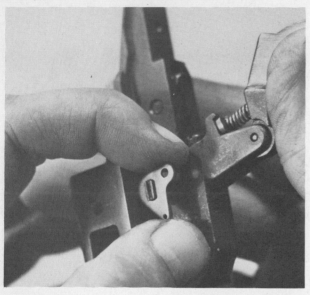

2. When replacing the safety button, note that its longer slope goes toward the front.

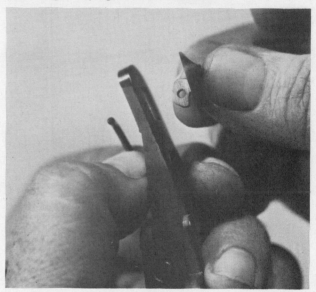

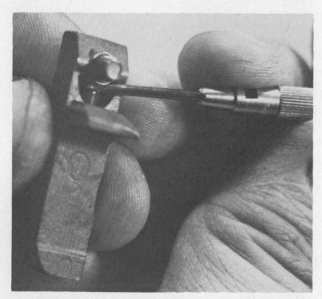

3. Before replacing the bolt stop on the receiver, insert a small screwdriver to jump the plunger back onto the edge of the post screw. During installation, take care that the plunger doesn't slip off the edge.

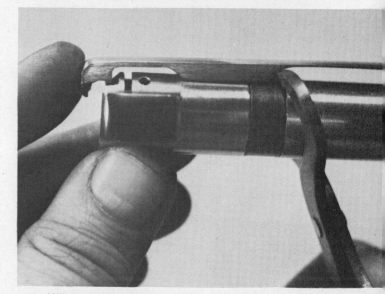

4. When replacing the extractor on the bolt, use the Brownells extractor pliers to compress the mounting ring flanges while sliding the extractor onto them. After it is well started into the flanges, use the pliers to lift the underlug at the front of the extractor onto the front edge of the bolt. Take care to lift the front of the extractor no more than is absolutely necessary for clearance.

SAKO FORESTER

Data:	Sako Forester
Origin:	Finland
Manufacturer:	Oy Sako, A. B., Riihimaki
Cartridges:	22-250, 243, 308
Magazine capacity:	5 rounds
Over-all length:	42 inches
Barrel length:	23 inches
Weight:	6½ pounds

A redesign of the original L-57 Forester of 1958 was done in 1960. It was designated the Model L-579, and was still called the Forester. In two varmint chamberings and one for medium game, it became very popular in its time, and is still treasured for the smoothness of its action. One of the reasons for this feature is a full-length guide on the bolt, mounted on a pivot-ring in the style of the old Mauser extractor. All Sako rifles are of outstanding quality in both materials and workmanship.

Disassembly:

1. Open the bolt and move it toward the rear, while pushing in the bolt stop, located at the left rear of the receiver. Remove the bolt from the rear of the receiver.

2. Grip the underlug of the cocking piece firmly in a vise, and pull the bolt body forward to clear the lug from the bolt sleeve. Turn the bolt until the lug on the bolt sleeve is aligned with the exit track on the bolt body, and separate the body from the sleeve and striker assembly.

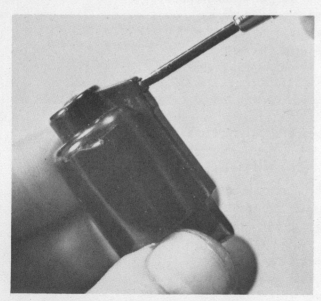

3. Back out the striker shaft lock screw, located on the underside of the cocking piece at the rear.

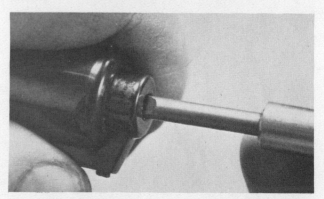

4. With a firm grip on the bolt sleeve and the striker spring, use a screwdriver to turn the screw-slotted rear tip of the striker shaft clockwise (rear view) until the striker is free from the cocking piece. The spring is under tension, so keep it under control.

5. Remove the cocking piece, bolt sleeve, and spring from the striker shaft toward the rear.

6. Remove the cocking piece from the bolt sleeve.

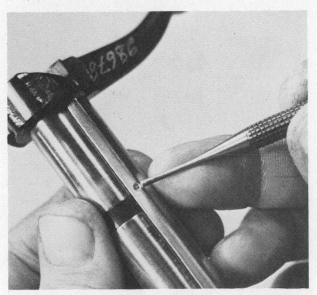

7. A small cross-pin retains the bolt guide on the side of the bolt. The mounting ring is not removed in normal takedown. If the guide is removed, take care not to lose the guide rib stop and spring, mounted inside the rib at the front.

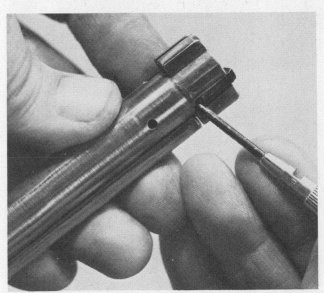

8. Insert a small screwdriver between the extractor and its plunger, and depress the plunger toward the rear, lifting the extractor out of its recess. **Caution:** *The spring is compressed, and can send the plunger quite a distance, so control the plunger and ease it out.*

9. Release the magazine floorplate latch, located in the front of the trigger guard, and open the floorplate. Flex the magazine spring away from the plate at the rear, and slide it rearward and out of its mounting slots. The magazine follower can be taken off the spring in the same manner.

10. Close and latch the floorplate, and remove the large vertical screws at the front of the magazine housing and at the rear of the trigger guard. Lift the action out of the stock.

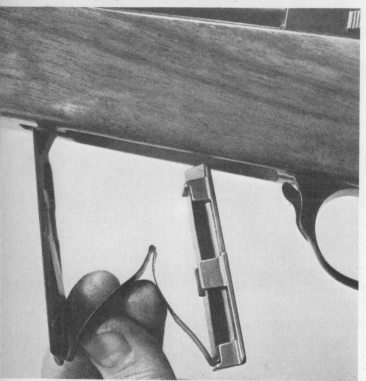

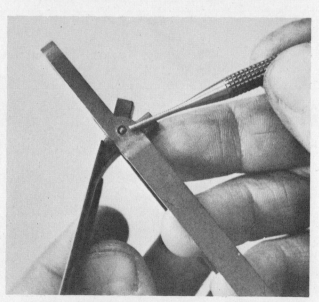

11. The trigger guard/magazine housing can now be removed downward. When this unit is removed, take care not to lose the steel spacer plates at the front and rear, inside the stock.

12. The magazine floorplate can be removed by drifting out its hinge cross-pin.

13. A small cross-pin at the front of the trigger guard retains the magazine floorplate latch and its spring. **Caution:** *The spring is very strong. Restrain the latch, and ease it off.*

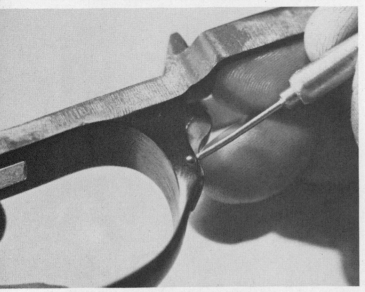

14. The magazine box is easily detached from its recess on the underside of the receiver.

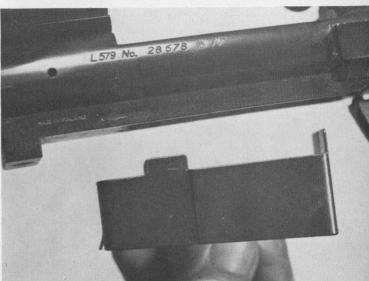

15. The bolt stop is retained by two screws on the left rear of the receiver, and is removed toward the left, along with its torsion spring. The bolt stop is also the ejector, and is pivoted inside its housing by a vertical pin. Drifting out the pin upward will free the stop/ejector and spring for removal.

16. Drift out the cross-pin at the upper front of the trigger housing.

17. Remove the trigger housing downward. Removal of this assembly will not disturb the trigger adjustment settings. Backing out the two screws on the right side of the housing will allow removal of the safety lever toward the right. **Caution:** *Removal of the safety will release the positioning ball and spring.* See the next step.

18. The safety ball and spring are mounted across the unit, and backing out this small headless screw on the left side will allow separate removal of the ball and spring.

19. After the safety is removed, driving out this cross-pin will allow the sear to be taken out upward.

20. Drifting out the trigger cross-pin, and the small stop pin behind it, will allow the trigger to be taken out downward. Unless the process of adjustment is known, the trigger adjustment nuts and screws should not be disturbed.

Reassembly Tips:

21. The safety cross-bolt is retained by a C-clip on the left side, and after its removal the safety bolt is taken out toward the right.

1. Note that the sides of the striker shaft at the rear have deep grooves lengthwise in the screw threads, and one of these must be aligned with the lock screw.

2. The degree of protrusion of the firing pin point from the breech face is governed by the level to which the striker shaft is turned on its threads during reassembly. Generally speaking, the rear tip of the striker shaft should be level with the rear of the cocking piece. To be more precise, the protrusion of the firing pin point at the front should be .055 inches, if you have a means of measuring this.

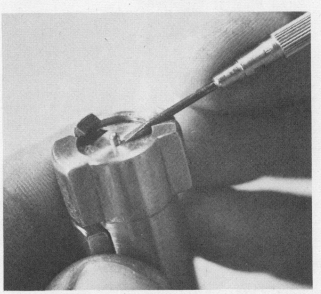

3. To properly check the protrusion, the bolt sleeve/striker assembly must be installed in the bolt. The photo shows an adjustment that has *far too much protrusion*. Adjustment can be made with the bolt fully assembled. After adjustment, be sure to tighten the lock screw securely. Note that the striker must be re-cocked before the bolt is put back in the gun.

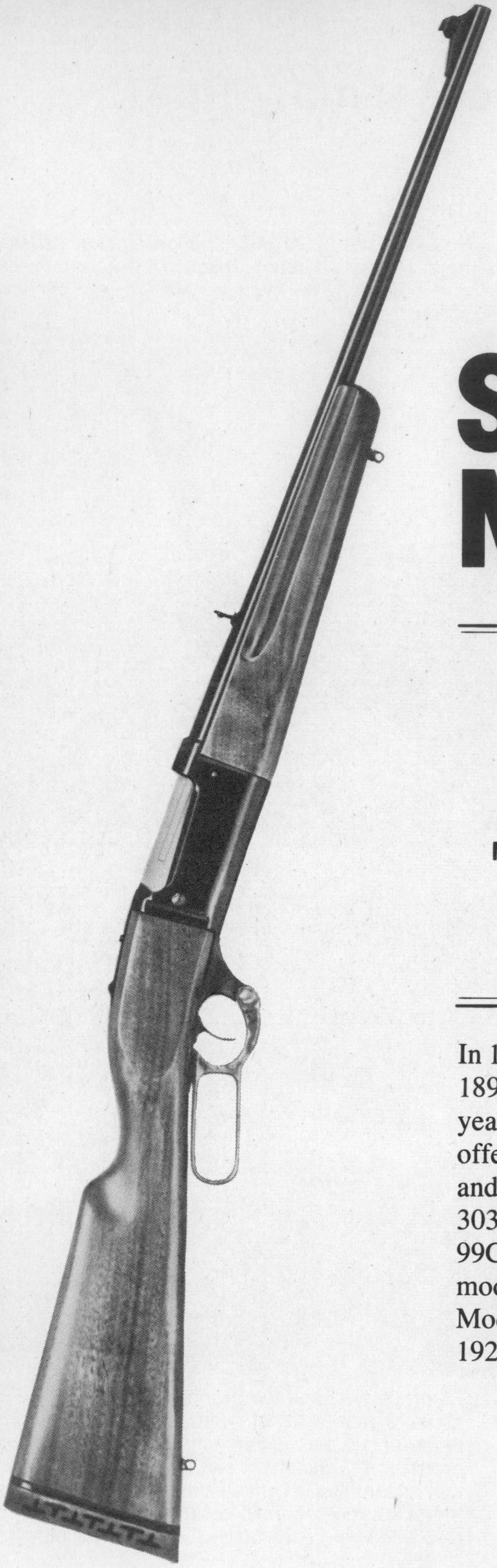

SAVAGE MODEL 99

Data:	Savage Model 99
Origin:	United States
Manufacturer:	Savage Arms Company Westfield, Massachusetts
Cartridges:	22-250, 243, 250 Savage, 300 Savage, 308 Winchester
Magazine capacity:	5 rounds
Over-all length:	39¾ to 41¾ inches
Barrel length:	22 and 24 inches
Weight:	6¾ to 7 pounds

In 1899, Arthur W. Savage modified his original design of 1895, and the Model 99 rifle was born. Today, some 80 years later, this gun is still in production. It has been offered in a number of versions or sub-models in the past, and at the present time five are available. Two calibers, the 303 Savage and 30-30, are no longer made. The Model 99C has a detachable box magazine, but the other current models have the unique Savage rotary magazine. The Model 99A, which replaced the original Model 99 in 1922, is the example shown here.

Disassembly:

1. Remove the buttplate to give access to the stock mounting bolt. Use a long screwdriver to remove the stock bolt, and take off the stock toward the rear. If the stock is tight, bump the front of the comb with the heel of the hand to start it.

2. Remove the vertical screw at the left rear of the lower receiver extension, and take off the bolt stop.

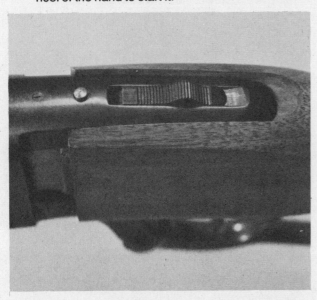

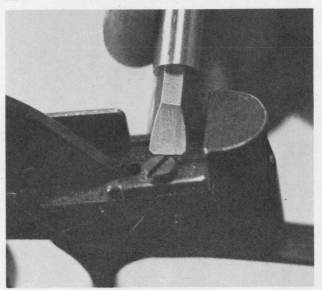

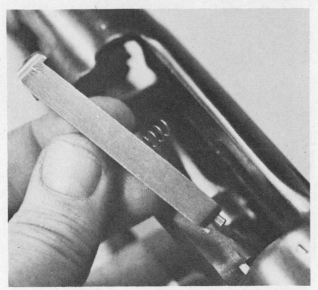

3. Open the action slowly, and restrain the cartridge cutoff, which will be released toward the right as the bolt clears it. Remove the cutoff and its spring toward the right.

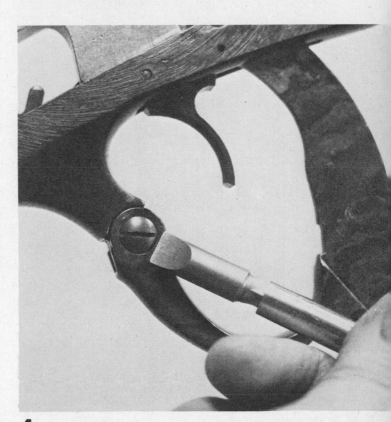

4. Remove the cap screw from the lever pivot.

5. Remove the lever pivot toward the right

6. Remove the front of the lever from its pivot loop and turn the rear arch slightly to clear its inner lug from the bolt. Remove the lever downward.

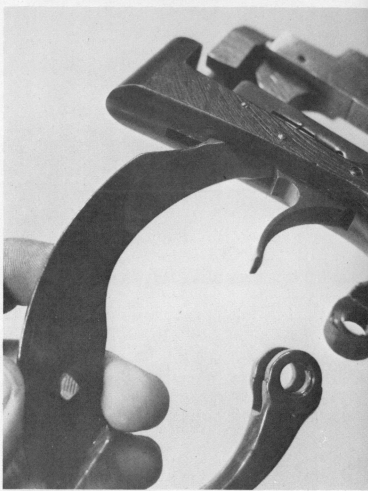

7. Move the bolt all the way to the rear, and pull the trigger to release the sear. Tip the sear to clear the bolt, and remove the bolt toward the left rear. Turn the lower rear of the breech-block (bolt) out toward the left to clear the receiver as the bolt is removed.

8. Remove the hammer and bushing screw from the left side of the bolt at the rear. Note that the screw is usually staked in place, and may require some effort in removal.

9. Remove the hammer and striker assembly toward the rear. Take care not to lose the hammer rebound spring, which will be released as the assembly is moved out to the rear.

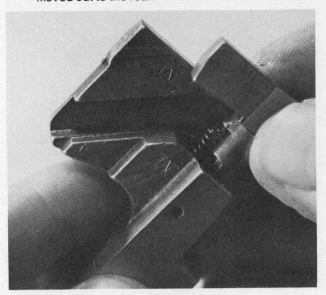

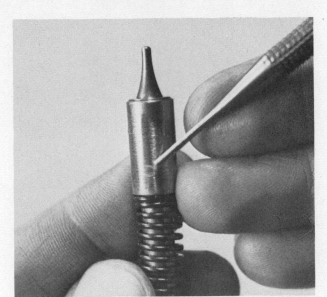

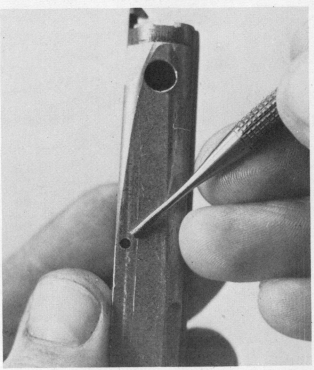

10. A vertical pin in the rear of the firing pin retains it on the front of the hammer shaft. Drifting out the pin will release the firing pin, hammer spring, and hammer bushing for removal toward the front. The pin is contoured at its ends to match the outside surface of the firing pin, and removal should be done only for repair purposes, not in normal takedown. If this unit is disassembled, proceed with caution, as the powerful hammer spring will be released.

11. The extractor is its own spring, and is retained by a vertical pin on the right side of the bolt. The pin is driven out upward, and the extractor is taken off toward the right.

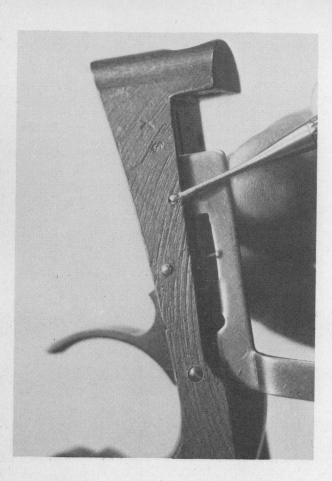

12. A small cross-pin at the rear of the lower receiver extension retains the safety slide. There is an access hole on the left side which allows the pin to be drifted out toward the right.

13. Move the saftey slide all the way to the rear, and tip it downward at the front and upward at the rear for removal.

14. Move the safety button all the way to the rear, and remove it from the top of the receiver.

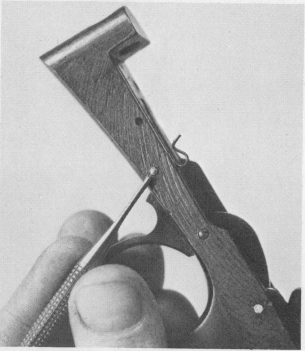

15. The safety positioning spring is retained by a short cross-pin, and there is an access hole on the left side of the receiver which allows the pin to be drifted out toward the right. Remove the spring upward.

16. Drift out the trigger cross-pin, and remove the trigger downward and toward the rear. **Caution:** *The trigger spring is under tension, so control it and ease it out.*

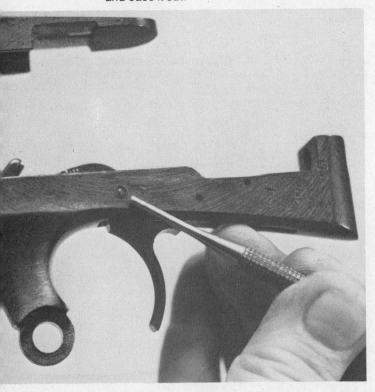

17. Drift out the short pin at the lower rear of the sear bracket. There is no access hole for this pin, so it is necessary to angle a drift punch to start the pin out, then remove it toward the right.

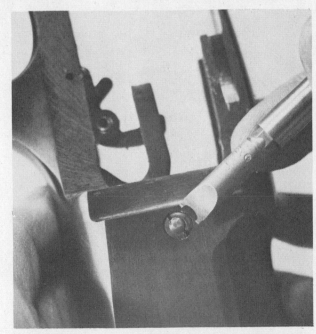

18. Removal of the sear bracket cross-screw and nut will require a special twin-pointed tool, easily made by cutting away the center of a screwdriver tip. If the screw is tight, it will be necessary to stabilize the slotted screw-head on the opposite side with a regular screwdriver as the nut is removed.

19. After the nut is removed, the screw must be unscrewed from the receiver and taken out toward the left.

20. Move the sear bracket assembly upward, out of its slot in the receiver, then remove it toward the rear.

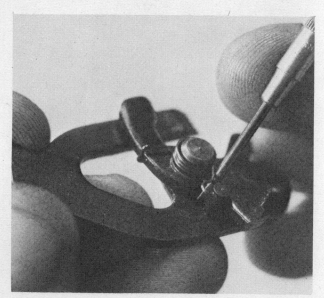

21. Unhook the lower arm of the sear spring from its groove on the stop stud, and allow it to swing around to the rear, relieving its tension. Remove the spring from the sear post.

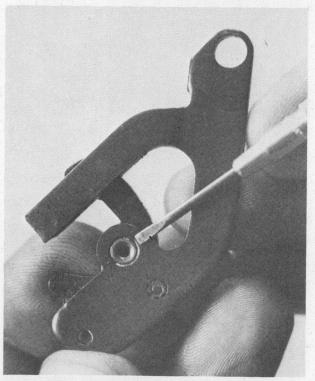

22. The sear is factory-riveted to the sear bracket, and should not be removed except for repair.

23. The hammer indicator can be removed from the top of the receiver by using a very small tool to lift the rear "T" of the indicator spring from its recess. Take out the spring toward the rear, and remove the indicator upward.

24. The fore-end is retained by a single vertical screw on its underside, and is taken off toward the front and downward.

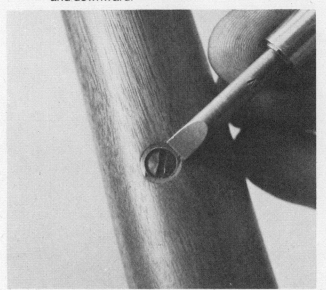

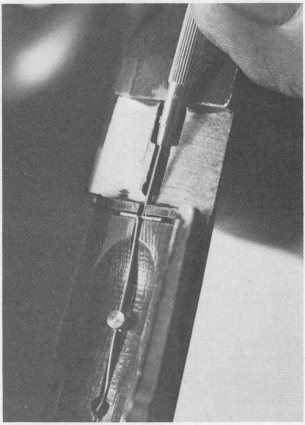

25. The same twin-pointed tool used to remove the sear bracket nut can also be used to take off the carrier spindle nut. **Caution:** *Disassembly of the magazine system of the Model 99 is not recommended unless this is necessary for repair, as reassembly is difficult for those not familiar with it. If disassembly is unavoidable, begin by removing the spindle nut.*

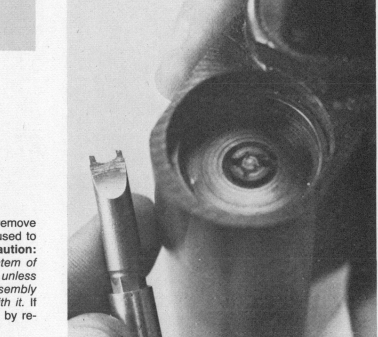

26. The carrier spindle head screw is located on the left side of the receiver near the front edge. Restrain the carrier spindle head against rotation, and remove the screw toward the left. Slowly release the tension of the carrier spring, allowing the head to rotate. The spindle head, carrier, and spring can now be removed toward the front, and the carrier spindle and spindle bracket are taken out toward the rear.

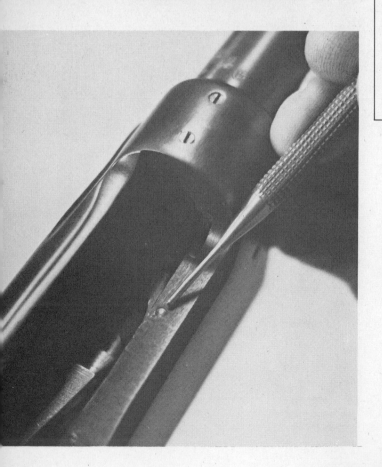

Reassembly Tips:

1. When replacing the safety slide, be sure the tip of the positioning spring engages its recess on the underside of the safety slide.

27. The cartridge guide is retained by two vertical pins in the lower edge of the ejection port, and is not removed in normal takedown. If necessary, the pins are driven downward and retrieved from inside the receiver, and the guide is taken off toward the left and upward.

2. When replacing the hammer and striker assembly in the bolt, remember to insert the rebound spring below the assembly just before pushing it into place for insertion of the retaining screw.

3. When replacing the lever pivot, note that there is a lug beneath its head on the left side that must be oriented to engage a recess in the lever loop on the receiver.

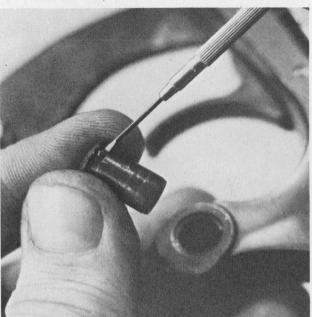

If the magazine has been dismantled, the carrier spring must be re-tensioned during reassembly by turning the spindle head before re-insertion of the cross-screw. The number of turns required depends on the strength of the spring, so this can't be specified here.

SAVAGE MODEL 110

Data:	Savage Model 110
Origin:	United States
Manufacturer:	Savage Arms Company Westfield, Massachusetts
Cartridges:	243, 22-250, 270, 308, 30-06, 300 Magnum, 7mm Remington Magnum
Magazine capacity:	4 rounds (3 in magnums)
Over-all length:	43 inches
Barrel length:	22 inches
Weight:	7 to 8⅝ pounds

Since its introduction in 1958, the Model 110 has been offered in a wide variety of sub-models, and several of these are still in production. This is one of the few rifles that is also available in a left-handed action, and the moderate price of the Model 110 has made it very popular. Recent additions to the line include a version with a detachable magazine, and a gun specially designed for metallic silhouette shooting. The instructions can be applied to all of the sub-models.

Disassembly:

1. Open the bolt, pull the trigger, and push down the sear lever on the right side of the receiver. Hold it down, and remove the bolt toward the rear.

2. With a coin or a large screwdriver, unscrew the large knob at the rear of the bolt. Once it is started, its knurled edge will allow it to be turned by hand. Remove the knob toward the rear.

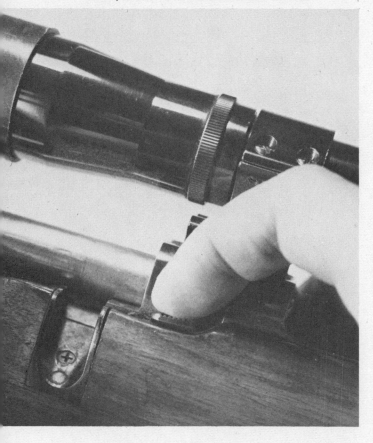

3. The attached cocking piece sleeve will come out with the knob as it is removed.

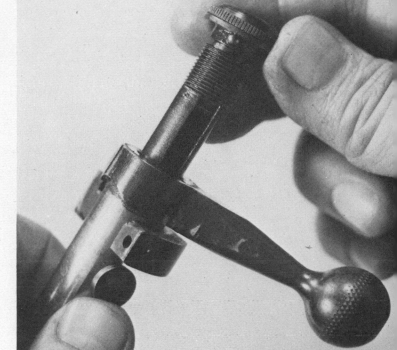

4. Remove the bolt handle toward the rear.

5. Remove the rear baffle piece toward the rear. If necessary, the two detent balls and spring can be removed from the baffle by pushing the inner ball outward until it aligns with the hole at the bottom of the baffle. The spring will then force both balls out. In normal disassembly, these parts are best left in place.

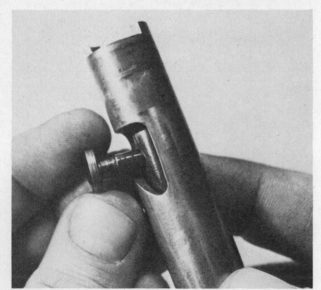

6. Remove the cocking piece pin from its hole in the side of the striker assembly.

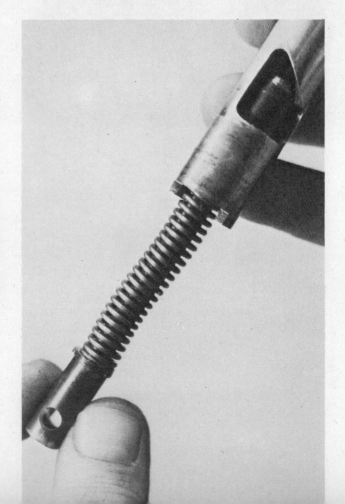

7. Remove the striker assembly from the rear of the bolt.

8. Grip the front of the striker firmly in a vise, insert a drift punch through the hole in the cocking piece, and unscrew the cocking piece from the rear tip of the striker shaft. **Caution:** *The striker spring is partially compressed, so control the parts and ease the tension slowly.* Take care not to disturb the striker stop nut at the front, as it controls the protrusion of the firing pin point at the bolt face. If the striker system does not need repair, it's best not to disassemble it.

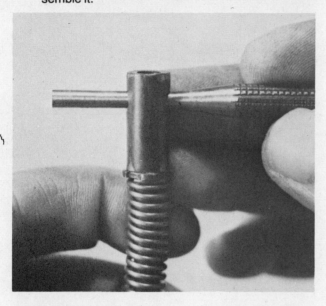

9. Drift out the bolt head retaining pin.

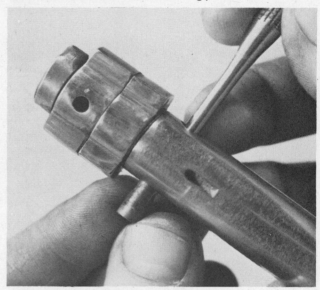

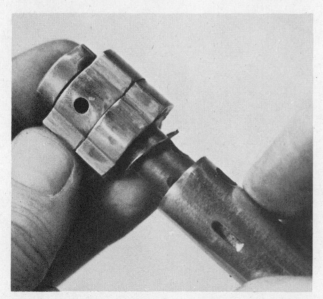

10. Remove the bolt head, baffle, and friction washer toward the front. The front baffle is easily taken off the bolt head toward the rear.

11. Insert a small screwdriver under the end of the extractor nearest the ejector slot, and twist the screwdriver toward the left, levering the extractor out of its groove and toward the front of the bolt.

12. Remove the large vertical screw on the underside at the front of the magazine floorplate. Remove the large vertical screw at the front of the trigger guard, in the rear tip of the magazine floorplate. Remove the floorplate and magazine insert downward, and take out the magazine spring and follower. Separate the action from the stock.

13. Depress the combination magazine latch and ejector housing upward, tip its lower end away from the magazine box, and remove the latch/housing, spring, and ejector downward.

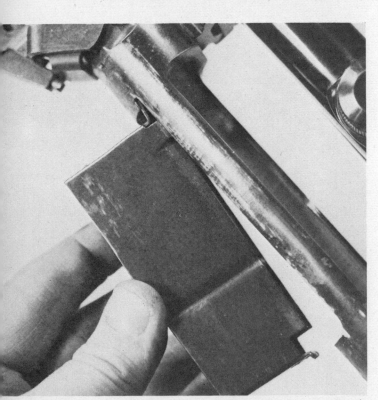

14. The magazine box can now be moved toward the rear, tipped down at the front, and removed forward and downward.

15. While restraining the sear spring, push out the sear pin toward the left.

16. Remove the sear downward and toward the front, along with its spring and bushing. Take care that the small bushing isn't lost.

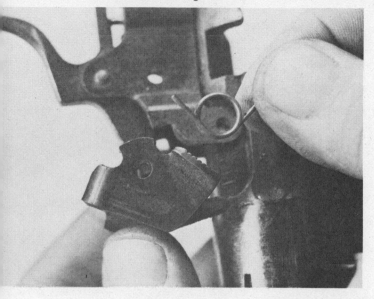

17. Tip the trigger housing down at the front, and unhook its rear lip from the underside of the receiver. Remove the trigger housing downward. After the housing is taken off, the small spring-steel trigger pull screw cover can be slid to the rear of its slot at the rear of the receiver, and removed. Remove the safety bearing pin from the housing.

18. Lift the safety block from the top of the trigger housing.

19. The trigger adjustment screws in the safety block need not be disturbed. The one at top center retains the trigger spring and its plunger, and can be taken out to allow removal of the spring and plunger upward.

20. Drifting out the trigger cross-pin will allow removal of the trigger from the housing. Note that this pin is held at center by a ball and spring in the front of the trigger, retained by a screw at the front. This screw should not be disturbed.

21. The barrel is retained in the receiver by a large grooved nut which also holds the recoil lug on the front of the receiver. In normal takedown, the barrel is best left in place.

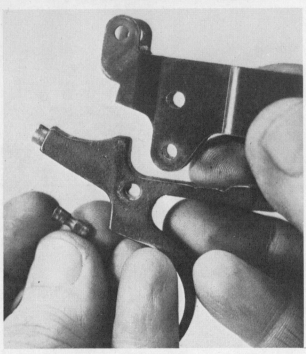

Reassembly Tips:

1. When replacing the sear system, insert the sear cross-pin from the left, and stop it short of crossing the spring recess. Insert the spring from the rear, and insert a drift punch into the spring bushing from the right to lever the bushing and spring into position for the cross-pin to be pushed through to the right.

2. When replacing the bolt head assembly, note that there is a recess in the rear tail of the bolt head and a depression and inside welt on the inside of the bolt body, and these must be aligned.

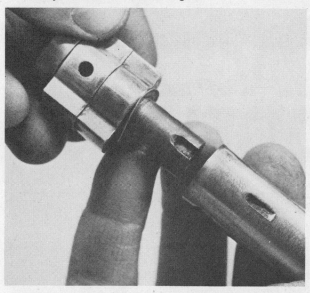

3. When replacing the bolt head retaining cross-pin, note that there is a hole at its center for passage of the firing pin, and this hole must be properly oriented as the cross-pin is installed.

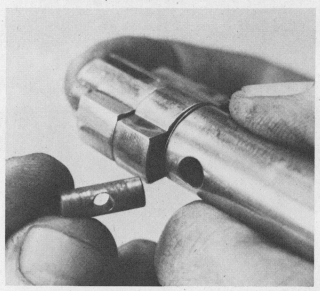

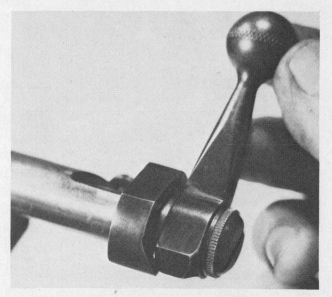

5. It is possible to install the rear baffle in reversed position. This photo shows its proper relationship with the bolt handle ring.

4. When replacing the bolt takedown screw, set the cocking piece pin in the cocked position, as shown. This will make tightening the screw a bit stiffer, but will leave the action cocked for re-insertion of the bolt into the receiver.

SAVAGE MODEL 340

Data: Savage Model 340
Origin: United States
Manufacturer: Savage Arms Company
Westfield, Massachusetts
Cartridges: 22 Hornet, 222, 30-30
Magazine capacity: 4 rounds (3 in 30-30)
Over-all length: 40 and 42 inches
Barrel length: 22 and 24 inches
Weight: 6½ pounds

The model 340 was intended to be an in-between gun, a low-priced bolt action repeater chambered for two varmint cartridges and one medium-game round. In this category it has gained wide acceptance since 1950, and it is still in production. For a short time, a carbine version was made in 30-30 only, with an 18½-inch barrel. The basic Model 340 design has been marketed as the Savage Model 342, the Stevens Model 322 and 325, and the Springfield Model 840. They are essentially the same.

Disassembly:

1. Remove the magazine. Pull the trigger all the way to the rear, beyond its normal let-off position, and hold it there. Open the bolt, and remove it toward the rear.

2. With a small brass hammer, tap the cocking lug out of its detent notch at the rear of the bolt, allowing the striker to go forward to the fired position, as shown.

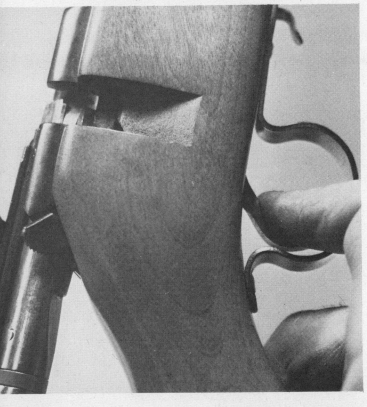

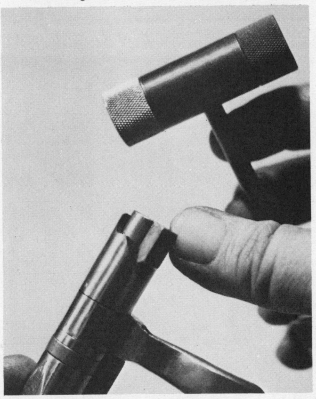

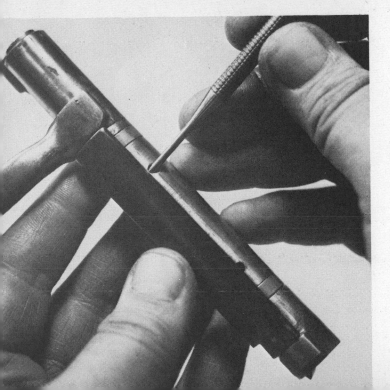

3. Drift out the cross-pin that retains the bolt head.

4. Remove the bolt handle and striker assembly toward the rear. If the assembly is tight, use a plastic hammer to tap it gently off.

5. Grip the front portion of the striker firmly in a vise, and push the bolt handle sleeve toward the front until the cocking piece is exposed. Remove the semi-circular key from the top of the cocking piece, and unscrew the cocking piece from the rear of the striker shaft. **Caution:** *Keep a firm grip on the bolt handle, as the striker spring is compressed.*

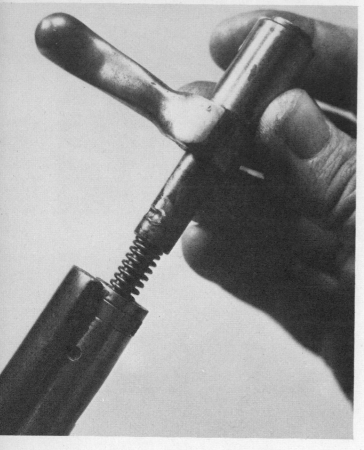

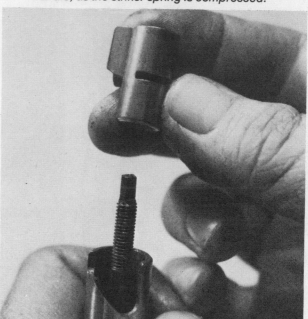

6. Slowly ease off the tension of the striker spring, and remove the striker and spring from the front of the bolt handle unit.

7. Some models of the 340 design have a clip-on extractor unit, and others, such as the one shown, have a hook-In type with a spring and plunger at the rear. To remove this type, restrain the plunger and spring, and pivot the extractor out toward the right and take it off. The clip-on type unit is simply pried out of its recess for removal.

8. The gas shield is retained on top of the bolt by two cross-pins, and mounted on twin rings which encircle the bolt. The cross-pins are usually staked in place, so if removal is necessary, be sure the shield is well-supported while driving out the pins.

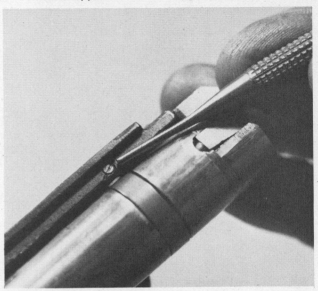

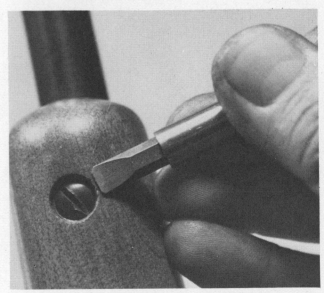

9. When the front gas shield cross-pin is drifted out, the gas shield key and its spring will be released along with the shield.

10. Remove the barrel band screw, located on the underside near the front of the stock.

11. Remove the main stock mounting screw, located on the underside in the front tip of the magazine plate. Separate the action from the stock.

12. To remove the barrel band, push the band nut toward the barrel, and disengage its side studs from the holes in the band. The band can then be taken off upward.

13. The magazine guide is retained on the underside of the receiver by a single screw, and the screw and guide are removed downward.

14. In the 22 Hornet version, the front magazine guide also contains a small cartridge ramp and a torsion spring for the ramp. Drifting out the cross-pin will release the ramp and spring for removal, but in normal takedown they are best left in place.

15. The cross-pins in the trigger housing that retain the trigger and sear mechanism have large heads on the right side and are semi-riveted on the left. It is not advisable to remove them in normal take-down. If necessary for repair, or if the trigger housing must be removed, the internal parts must be taken out, as the two vertical retaining screws for the housing are obscured by the parts. Drifting out the pin shown will release the trigger and its spring for removal toward the rear and down-ward.

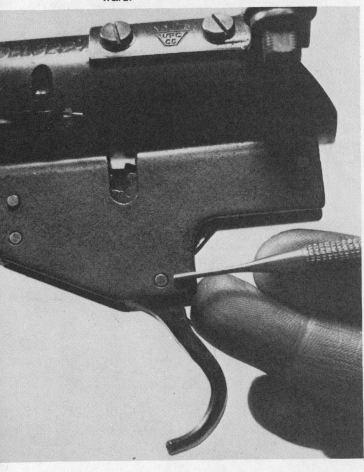

16. Drifting out the cross-pin at the upper rear of the trigger housing will release the sear and its spring for removal downward and toward the rear. The spring is under tension, so control it and ease it out.

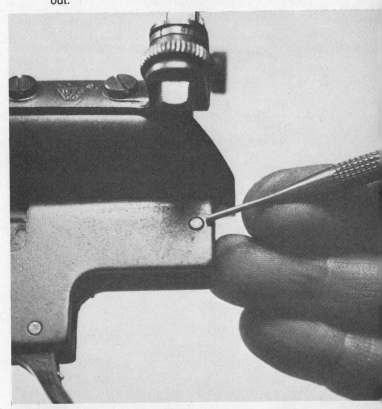

17. Drifting out the lower cross-pin at the front of the trigger housing will release the sear lever for removal downward. The upper pin holds the combination sear lever bracket and magazine stop in place, and its re-moval is not necessary.

18. Remove the safety lever screw, and take off the safety toward the right.

19. When the safety lever is removed, take care not to lose the small safety positioning ball and spring. If they do not come out freely, there is an access hole on the inside of the bolt tunnel in the receiver for insertion of a tool to nudge them out. Removal of the screw on the right side of the housing will allow the main safety block to be taken off toward the right.

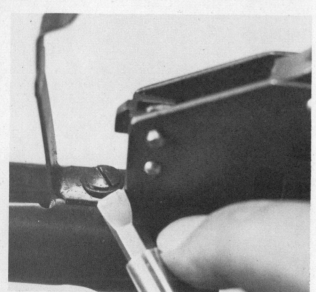

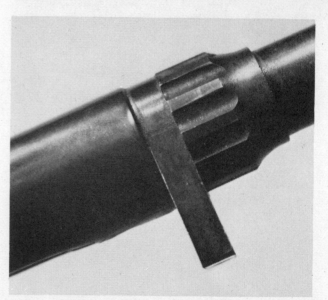

20. After the other parts are removed from the trigger housing, the vertical screws at the front and center will be accessible, and the trigger housing can be removed downward. The magazine catch screw can also be removed, and the catch taken off downward.

21. The barrel is retained in the receiver by a deeply grooved lock nut, requiring a special wrench which is not routinely available. It can be loosened or retightened by using a hammer and non-marring punch in one of the grooves, working in an area normally covered by the stock. Removal of the nut will allow the barrel to be taken out toward the front, and the recoil lug will also be freed for removal. In normal takedown, this system should be left in place.

22. Insert a screwdriver beneath the upper collar of the ejector pivot pin, and pry it out upward and toward the left. The ejector and its spring will be released for removal from their slot in the side of the receiver.

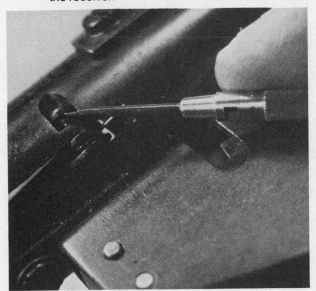

Reassembly Tips:

1. When replacing the cocking piece on the rear of the striker shaft, note that the degree of advancement on the threads controls the protrusion of the firing pin point from the bolt face. Check this by inserting the rear portion of the bolt, with the striker in the fired position, into the front portion of the bolt. If the protrusion is more than the amount shown, turn the cocking piece for adjustment.

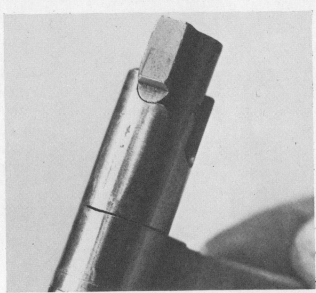

2. Before the reassembled bolt can be put back into the receiver, the gas shield must be aligned with the forward lug of the bolt and the bolt handle base, and the striker must be cocked. When the striker is in the position shown, the bolt can be re-inserted.

SCHMIDT-RUBIN

Data: Swiss Schmidt-Rubin
Origin: Switzerland
Manufacturer: Swiss Military Arsenals
Cartridge: 7.5mm Swiss
Magazine capacity: 6 rounds
Over-all length: 51.65 inches
Barrel length: 30.75 inches
Weight: 10⅛ pounds

The Swiss rifle of 1889 was designed by Colonel Rudolf Schmidt, director of the Swiss Federal Arsenal, and its 7.5mm cartridge was designed by Colonel Eduard Rubin, director of the Swiss Federal Ammunition Factory. The design of this rifle was modified several times during its long period of manufacture (68 years!), and the version most familiar in the U.S. is probably the Model 1911, the one shown in the photos. Although not practical from a military standpoint, the straight-pull bolt mechanism of this rifle is a mechanical work of art.

Disassembly:

1. Remove the magazine. Depress the bolt stop, located on the right side of the receiver, hold it down, and remove the bolt assembly toward the rear.

2. Pull back the cocking piece ring and turn it, setting its underlug halfway between the two rectangular openings in the rear of the bolt endpiece.

3. Turn the locking sleeve clockwise (rear view) until the cam rod and bolt handle unit can be moved forward and detached from the bolt, as shown.

5. Remove the locking sleeve toward the rear.

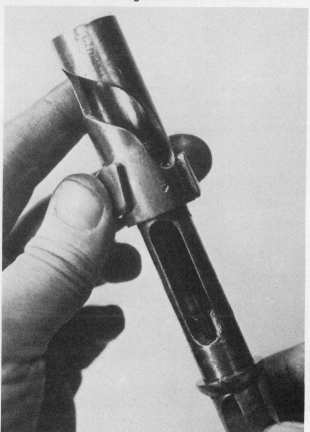

4. Taking care not to move the striker lug from its position between the two openings, unscrew the bolt endpiece and remove it toward the rear.

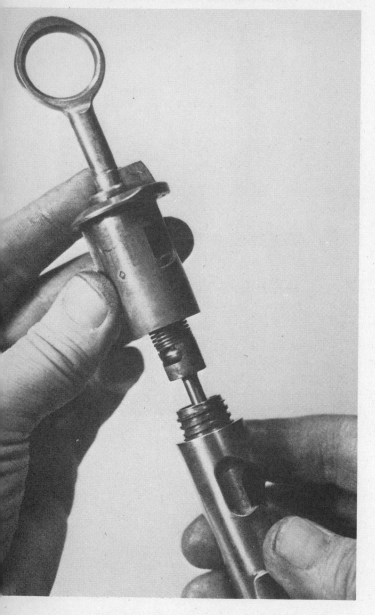

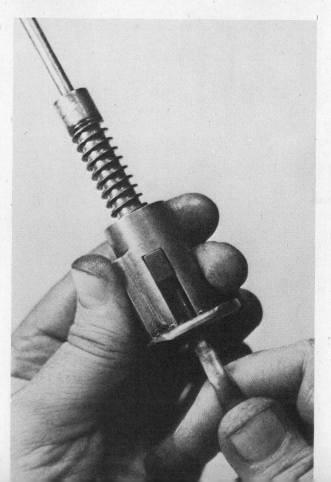

6. With a firm grip on the bolt endpiece, turn the cocking piece back until its underlug aligns with the lower opening, and allow the striker lug to move forward into its slot, partially relieving the tension of the striker spring.

7. With a firm grip on the striker spring, pull it back away from the rear of the firing pin, and detach the firing pin from the end of the striker rod toward the side. Remove the striker spring toward the front.

8. Remove the cocking piece from the rear of the bolt endpiece.

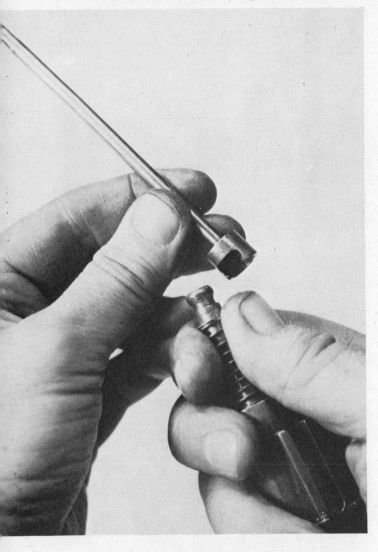

9. Wedge a screwdriver under the extractor in the opening provided at the rear, raising it just enough to lift its underlug out of its slot in the bolt. Push up the extractor beak at the front, just enough to clear the edge of the bolt, and rotate the extractor clockwise (top view) until it can be lifted off. **Caution:** *Be sure to raise each end only enough for clearance. Unless removal is necessary for repair, leave the extractor in place.*

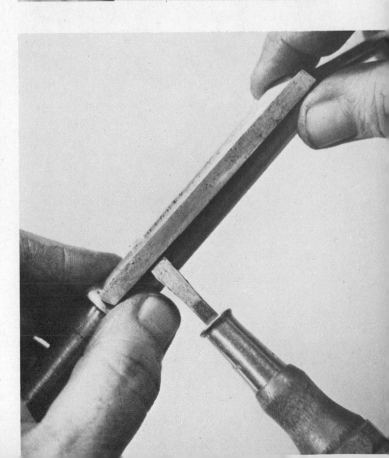

10. Remove the vertical screw on the right side of the front barrel band. Open the hinged band, and take it off.

11. Take out the vertical screw on the right side of the rear barrel band, depress the spring latch on the underside of the stock, and slide the band off toward the front. The upper handguard wood can now be removed from the top of the barrel.

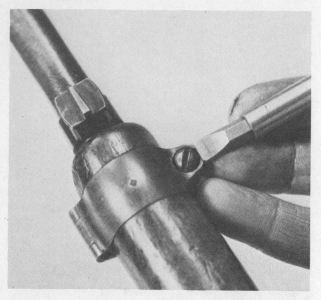

12. Remove the vertical screw at the front of the magazine opening. Remove the vertical screw at the rear of the magazine opening.

13. Remove the vertical screw at the rear of the trigger guard, and separate the action from the stock.

14. The trigger guard and magazine plate can be removed at this point, but these are usually very tightly fitted, so take care not to chip the recess in the wood. The trigger guard can be removed by unscrewing it from the plate.

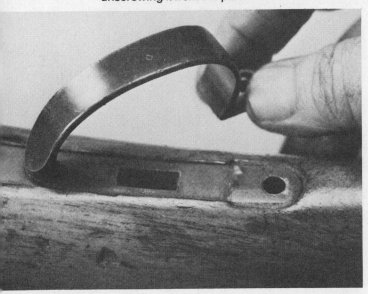

15. To remove the bolt stop and its spring, drive the pivot pin inward. There is a recess for it on the underside of the receiver, and the pin is not removed, just driven out of the way. The bolt stop and its spring are removed downward.

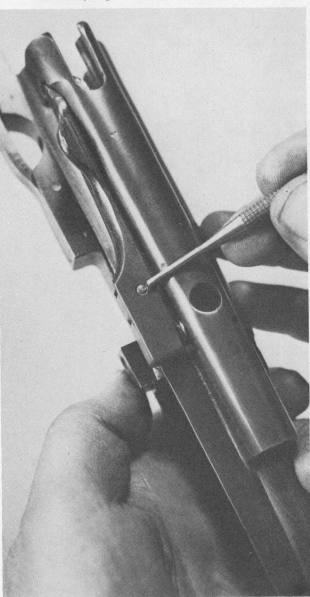

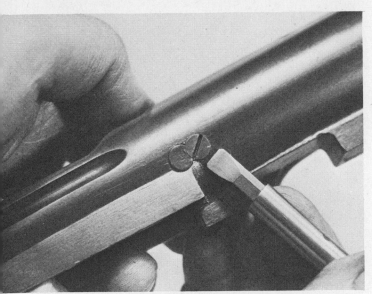

16. Remove the ejector lock screw, and take out the ejector toward the left. If it is tight, it can be nudged with a drift punch from inside the receiver.

17. To remove the trigger and sear assembly, push the front arm of the sear inward (upward) and toward the rear until its stops, then pull the trigger, and the assembly will be detached from the receiver.

18. Remove the trigger and sear assembly from the bottom of the receiver, and remove the sear spring from its recess. The sear pivot pin is not removed from the receiver.

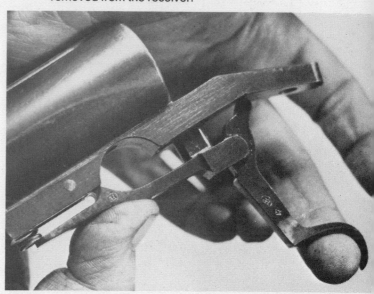

19. The trigger and sear can be separated by drifting out the trigger cross-pin.

Reassembly Tips:

1. When replacing the trigger and sear assembly, set the front tip of the sear on the sear spring, and push the assembly inward and toward the front. Be sure it snaps audibly into place, and is all the way to the front of its recess, as shown.

2. When replacing the locking sleeve on the bolt, note that the locking lugs must be at the front.

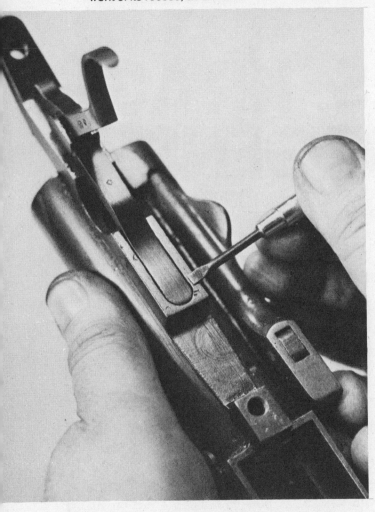

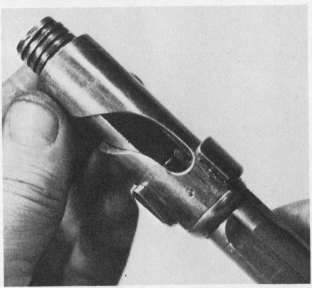

3. For replacement of the cam rod and bolt handle unit, the bolt sleeve and endpiece must be in the position shown.

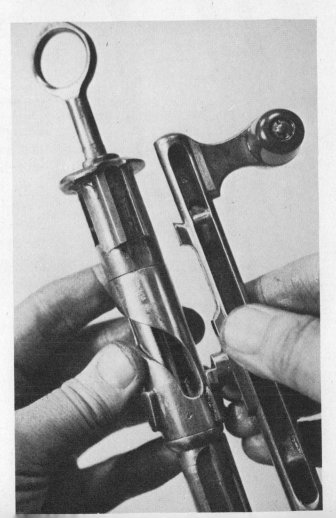

U.S. KRAG-JORGENSEN

Data: Krag-Jorgensen
Origin: United States
Manufacturer: Springfield Arsenal
Cartridge: 30-40 Krag
Magazine capacity: 5 rounds
Over-all length: 49.1 inches (rifle), 41.2 inches (carbine)
Barrel length: 30 inches (rifle), 22 inches (carbine)
Weight: 9.3 pounds (rifle), 7¾ pounds (carbine)

Designed by Ole Hermann Johannes Krag and Erik Jorgensen at Konigsberg Arsenal in Norway, the Krag rifle was the U.S. military standard from 1892 to 1903. The Krag was the first U.S. military rifle to use a cartridge loaded with smokeless powder, and saw action in the Spanish-American War, the Phillippine Insurrection, and the Boxer Rebellion in China. Two points of the design are particularly notable—its unique magazine system, and the ultra-smoothness of its well-supported bolt.

Disassembly:

1. To remove the bolt, open it and move it all the way to the rear. While lifting the front of the extractor, turn the bolt handle over toward the left, beyond its usual bolt-open position. The extractor will climb out of the open track in the upper rear of the receiver, and the bolt can then be withdrawn toward the rear.

2. To remove the striker assembly from the rear of the bolt, pull back on the striker knob and turn the sleeve assembly toward the left (rear view) until the front extension of the sleeve clears its lug on the rear of the bolt body. Keep a thumb against the back of the safety lever to restrain the spring tension, as the sleeve will be pushed toward the rear when the lug is cleared. Remove the sleeve and striker assembly toward the rear.

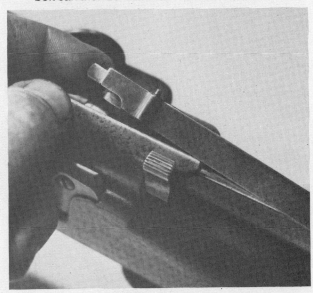

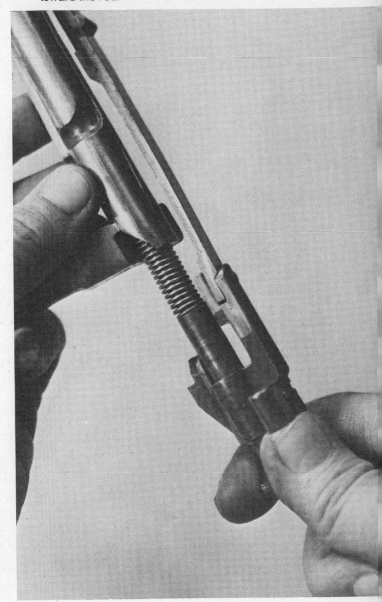

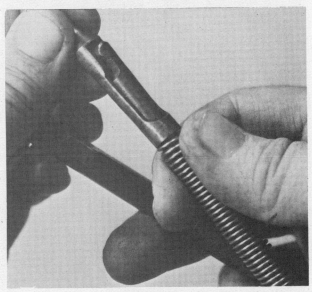

3. To remove the firing pin from the front of the striker rod, grip the spring firmly to restrain it, and tip the firing pin off its doll-head mount, then remove it toward the front. **Caution:** *The striker spring is under compression. Keep it under control, and ease off the tension slowly.*

4. Remove the firing pin and striker spring toward the front.

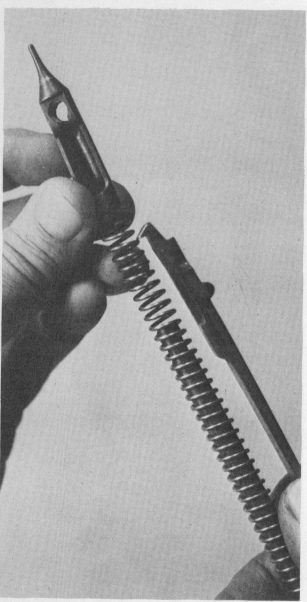

5. Remove the striker knob and rod unit toward the rear.

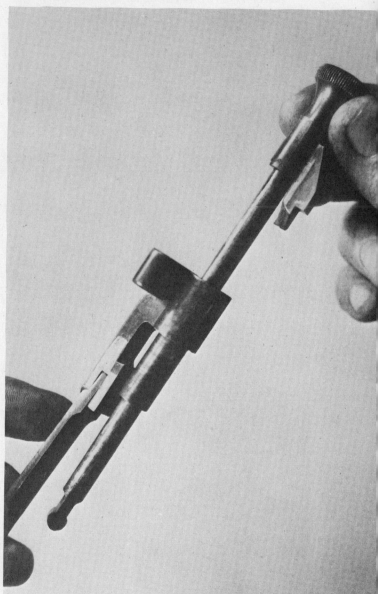

6. To remove the safety lever, turn it up to the middle position and use a non-marring hammer to tap it out toward the rear. Note that the safety plunger and spring, mounted inside the safety lever, will be released when they clear the rear of the sleeve, so take care that they aren't lost.

7. The extractor can be removed by drifting out its vertical mounting pin. Note that the pin must be drifted out downward, and take care that the front extension of the sleeve is well-supported, to avoid deformation or breakage of the extractor loops.

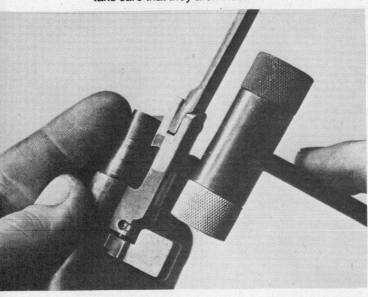

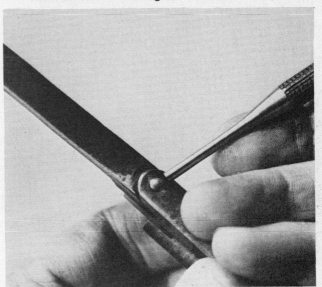

8. Remove the barrel band screw, take off the sling loop, and slide the barrel band off toward the front. Note that the gun shown is a modified rifle. If the gun has a full military stock, it will be necessary to first remove the front stock endpiece/bayonet mount. If the gun is an original carbine version, depressing a latch bar on the right side will release the band. Removal of the rear band will also release the wood handguard piece, if present, to be taken off forward and upward.

9. Remove the vertical screws on the underside at the front and rear of the trigger guard. Take off the guard downward, and separate the action from the stock. Take care to move the action straight upward during removal.

10. Removal of the magazine gate hinge bar must be done carefully, as these are often deformed or broken if certain precautions are not taken. Grip the receiver lightly in a padded vise, exerting slight pressure on the gate to relieve tension on the hinge bar. The front head of the bar is then turned clockwise (front view), swinging its locking plate out of its notch on the receiver. The hinge bar is then removed toward the front. It may be necessary to use a hammer and drift punch on the rear tip of the hinge bar to start it out, but use no extreme force. Remove the hinge bar toward the front.

11. Remove the magazine gate toward the right.

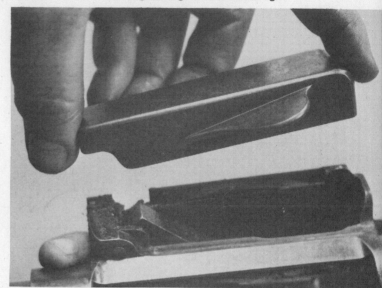

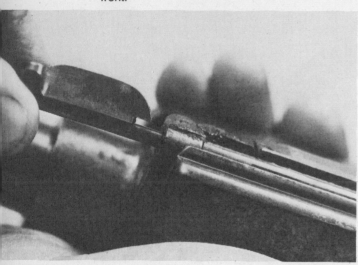

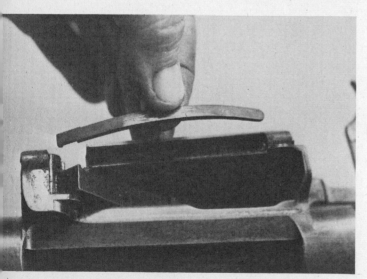

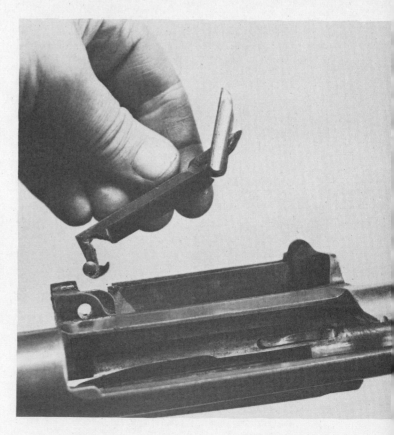

12. Lift the magazine spring out of its recess and remove it.

13. Swing the carrier and follower assembly out to the right, then remove it downward, disengaging its pivot post from the vertical hole in the receiver. The follower is mounted on the end of the carrier arm by a vertical pin. In normal takedown, this assembly is best left intact.

14. Move the trigger forward, to tip the rear of the sear down out of its slot in the receiver, and move the trigger and sear assembly toward the left, out of their pivot-recess. **Caution:** *When the sear spring, mounted in the lower front of the sear, clears the edge of the receiver, it will be released toward the front, and it is compressed. Control it, and ease it out.* Drifting out the cross-pin at the top of the trigger will allow separation of the trigger and sear.

15. To remove the magazine cutoff, it is necessary to insert a small screwdriver to depress the plunger and spring into the cutoff handle while moving the cutoff toward the rear and out of the receiver. **Caution:** *The plunger and spring will be released as they clear the rear of the receiver. Restrain them and ease them out.*

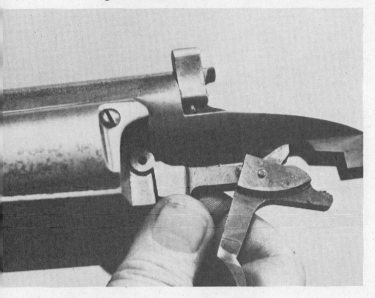

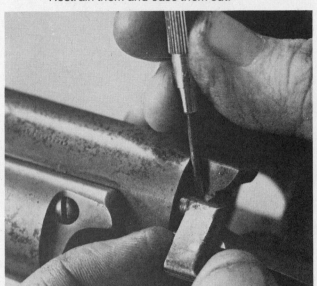

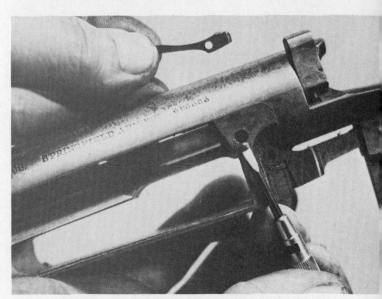

16. A single screw retains the receiver sideplate on the left side. After the screw is taken out, the sideplate is tipped outward and removed toward the rear.

17. Removal of the side-plate will expose a small pin near the screw-hole. The pin has a cannelure at its head to facilitate removal. Lifting out this pin toward the left will release the ejector for removal from the floor of the bolt track inside the receiver.

Reassembly Tips:

1. When replacing the magazine spring, note that the square off-set end of the spring goes at the front. Be sure the tip of the spring properly engages the lower lobe of the carrier lever.

2. When replacing the magazine gate and hinge bar, once again grip the receiver lightly in a padded vise, slightly compressing the assembly against the tension of the magazine spring. Be certain that the gate is properly aligned before inserting the hinge bar, and use no extreme force. When the bar is fully reinserted, turn it counter-clockwise (front view) until its lock-plate snaps back into its shelf on the receiver, as shown.

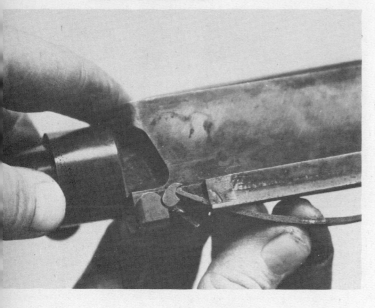

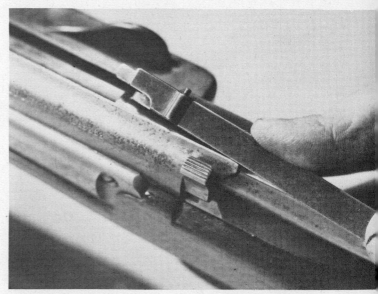

3. When replacing the sleeve and striker assembly in the bolt, push on the rear of the safety lever to move the sleeve forward, against the tension of the spring, until the sleeve can be turned clockwise (rear view) onto its lug at the rear of the bolt. Before the bolt can be re-inserted in the receiver, the striker must be re-cocked by pulling the knob to the rear and turning it clockwise until the front edge of the striker engages its recess at the edge of the cocking ramp, as shown.

4. When replacing the bolt in the receiver, align its forward lug with the open track in the upper rear of the receiver, and move it forward until it can be turned down to the right, following the slope of the inner shoulder of the receiver. At the same time, exert leftward and downward pressure on the extractor as the bolt is turned. The extractor will snap into the open track, and the bolt can then be moved forward.

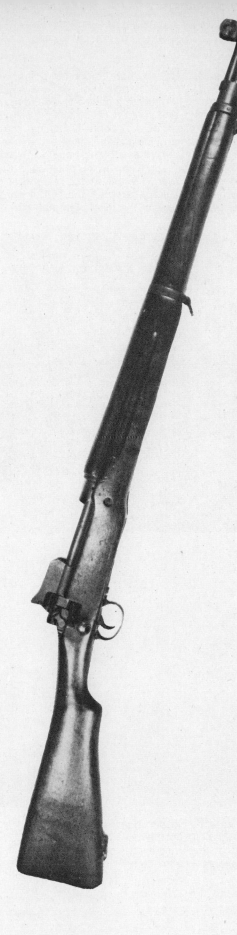

U.S. MODEL 1917 ENFIELD

Data: U.S. P-17 Enfield

Origin: United States

Manufacturers: Remington Arms Company, at Ilion, New York, and Eddystone, Pennsylvania, and Winchester in New Haven, Connecticut

Cartridge: 30-06

Magazine capacity: 5 rounds

Over-all length: 46.3 inches

Barrel length: 26 inches

Weight: 9 pounds

This rifle was originally developed by the British between 1910 and 1913, and was chambered for an experimental 276-cal. rimless round. When issued as a substitute standard gun for the British forces, the chambering was for the regular 303 British round, and the rifle was called the P-14 Enfield. When the U.S. entered World War I, the supply of 1903 Springfield rifles on hand was small, and a number of P-14 Enfields, left over from British contracts, were converted to 30-06, and designated as the U.S. Model 1917, or P-17 Enfield.

Disassembly:

1. Open the bolt, and pull the bolt stop outward, holding it out while removing the bolt toward the rear.

2. For bolt disassembly, do not remove the bolt from the receiver. Lift the bolt handle about half-way, and push forward on it, opening a gap between the rear of the bolt sleeve and the front of the cocking piece. Insert a thin piece of steel (a penny works fine, too) into the gap, trapping the cocking piece at the rear. In some guns, pushing the half-lifted handle forward will not open an adequate gap. In this case, open the bolt and move it toward the rear, turn the safety back to the on-safe position, then push the bolt forward until the gap opens and the steel plate can be inserted.

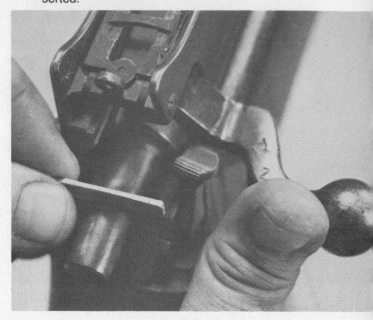

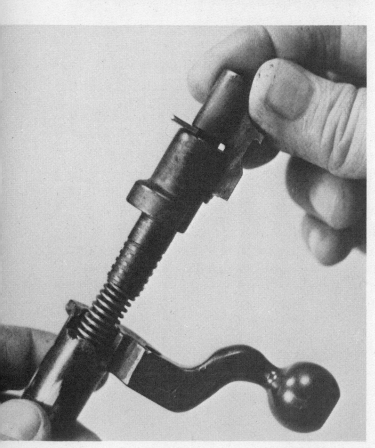

3. Taking care not to dislodge the steel plate, remove the bolt from the receiver as described in step #1, and unscrew the bolt sleeve and striker assembly from the rear of the bolt.

4. With the front of the striker gripped firmly in a vise, push the bolt sleeve toward the front, and remove the steel plate inserted earlier. Push the sleeve forward until the rear edge clears the front of the cocking lug, and rotate the cocking piece one quarter turn in either direction. Remove the cocking piece from the rear of the striker shaft. **Caution:** *Keep the bolt sleeve under control, as the powerful striker spring is compressed.*

5. Release the spring tension slowly, and remove the bolt sleeve and striker spring toward the rear.

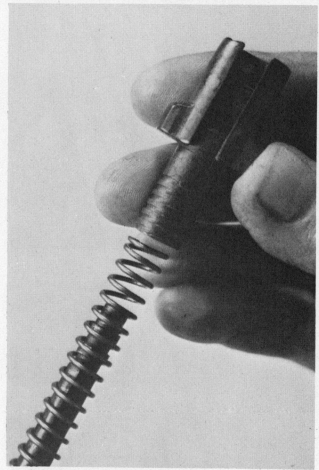

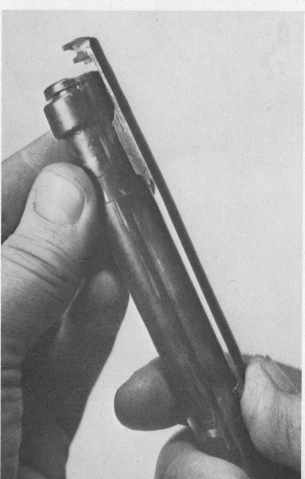

6. Turn the extractor clockwise (rear view) until it is aligned with the gas port, and its front under-lug is out of the groove at the front, and push it off its mount toward the front.

7. Insert a drift punch in the hole at the rear of the magazine floorplate, and depress the floorplate latch. Slide the plate slightly toward the rear, and remove it downward, along with the magazine spring and follower. The spring is easily detached from the floorplate and follower by sliding it out of its mounting slots.

8. Remove the cross-screw in the front barrel band, slide it toward the front, and take off the front upper handguard wood.

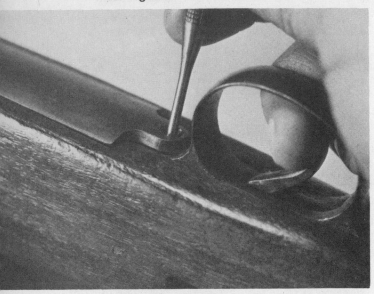

9. Drift out the cross-pin in front of the rear barrel band, and move it forward off the stock. It may be necessary to also loosen the sling loop cross-screw at the bottom of the band. The rear upper handguard can now be moved forward, and taken off upward.

10. Remove the screw on the underside, in the front tab of the trigger and magazine housing. Remove the screw on the underside at the rear of the trigger guard, and separate the action from the stock. The magazine box can be removed from the stock, and the guard and magazine housing can be taken off downward.

11. Drifting out the cross-pin in the guard will allow removal of the magazine floorplate latch and its spring upward.

12. Drifting out the cross-pin in the front sight will allow removal of the front sight assembly toward the front. This unit is usually tight, and may have to be nudged off with a hammer and nylon drift. Take care not to lose the front sight key, which will be released as the sight is removed. The front band, rear band, and the rear upper handguard ring can now be taken off toward the front.

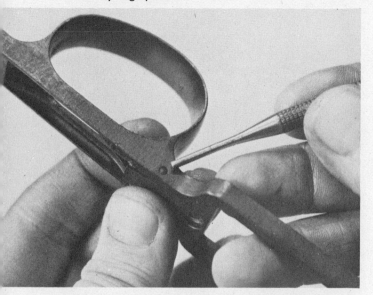

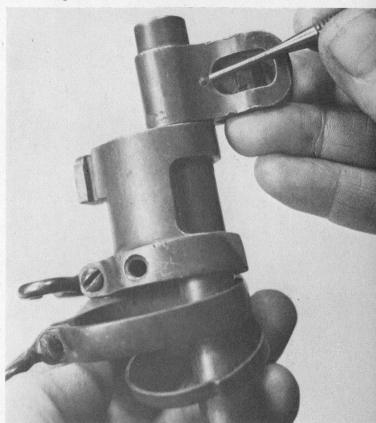

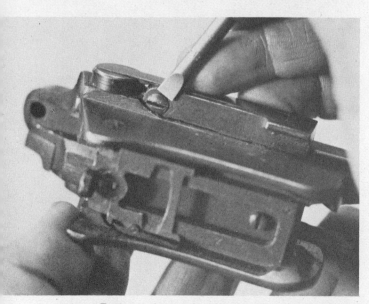

13. Remove the vertical screw that retains the bolt stop, at the left rear of the receiver, and take off the bolt stop and ejector assembly toward the left. The spring rest plug can also be taken out toward the left.

14. Tip the rear tail of the bolt stop spring inward, to lift its front hooks from inside the stop, and remove the spring and ejector toward the rear.

15. Remove the small cross-screw at the right rear of the receiver, and take off the safety lever retainer toward the rear.

16. With the safety lever in the on-safe position (toward the rear), insert a small-diameter drift punch to depress the safety plunger and spring, and remove the safety toward the right. Restrain the plunger and spring, and ease them out. As the safety is moved toward the right, the drift must be removed to allow the cross-piece to pass, then is re-inserted to restrain the plunger and spring.

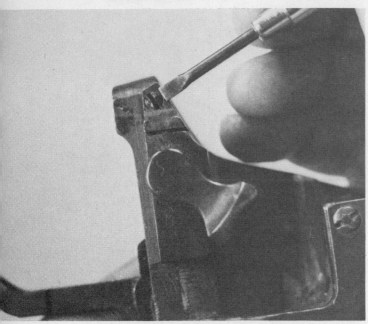

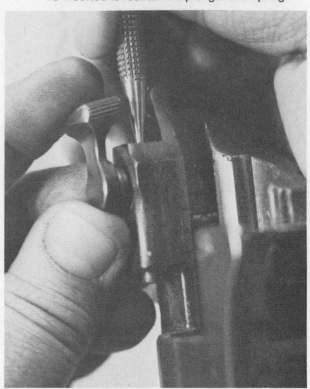

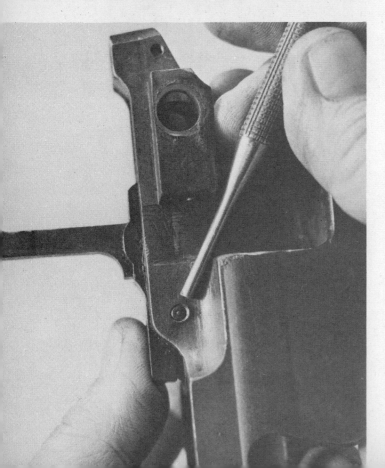

17. Drift out the sear cross-pin toward the left. Exert upward pressure on the front of the sear, and the cross-pin can be pushed out more easily.

18. Remove the sear, trigger, and sear spring downward. Drifting out the trigger cross-pin will allow separation of the trigger from the sear.

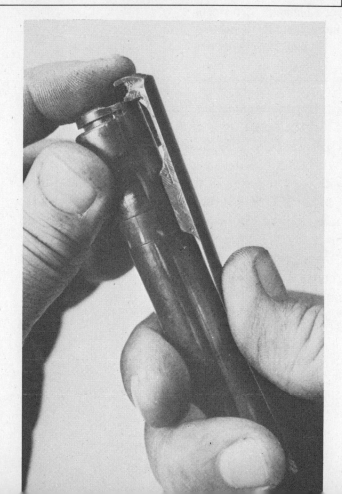

Reassembly Tips:

1. When replacing the safety lever, insert a slim tool from the rear to depress the safety plunger and spring while the safety is inserted.

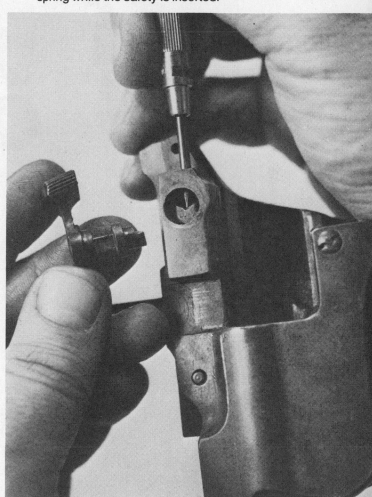

2. When replacing the extractor, after it is started back onto its flanges on the mounting ring, depress the tail of the extractor while lifting the beak at the front, to clear its underlug over the front edge of the bolt. Lift it only enough to clear.

U.S. 30 M-1 CARBINE

Data:	U.S. 30 M1 Carbine
Origin:	United States
Manufacturers:	Winchester, IBM, General Motors, and several other contractors
Cartridge:	30 Carbine
Magazine capacity:	15 or 30 rounds
Over-all length:	35.6 inches
Barrel length:	18 inches
Weight:	5½ pounds

Designed by an engineering group at Winchester, the Carbine was adopted as a U.S. military arm in 1941. Several sub-models were developed later, such as the M1A1 with folding stock, and the M2 selective fire version. With the exception of the parts that pertain to their special features, the instructions for the standard M1, given here, can be applied to the others. Early and late Carbines will have some small differences, such as the change from a flat-topped bolt to a round one, different rear sight, etc., but none of the changes affect the take-down to any great degree.

Disassembly:

1. Remove the magazine, and cycle the action to cock the internal hammer. Loosen the cross-screw in the lower flanges of the barrel band. It should be noted that if a screwdriver is not available, the rim of a cartridge case can be used to turn the specially-shaped screw head.

2. Depress the barrel band latch, located on the right side, and slide the band and bayonet mount unit toward the front. Move the upper handguard wood forward, and lift it off. Tip the action upward at the front, unhooking its rear lug, and lift it out of the stock.

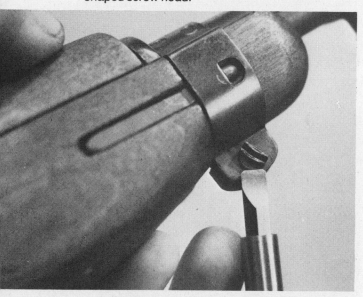

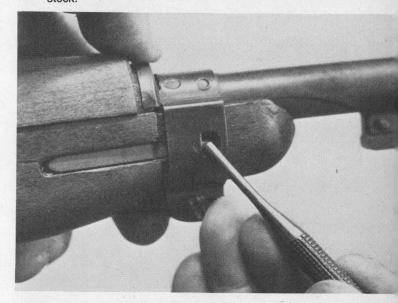

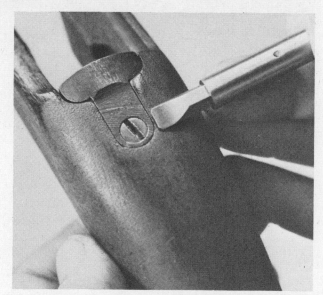

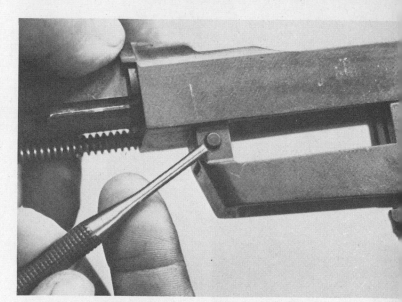

3. The barrel band latch can be removed by drifting its cross-post out toward the right, using the small access hole on the left side of the stock. Backing out the vertical screw in the tail of the recoil plate will allow removal of the plate upward.

4. Push out the cross-pin at the front of the trigger housing, move the housing forward, out of its slots at the rear, and remove it downward.

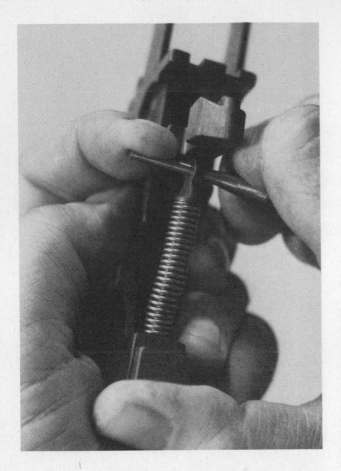

5. Restrain the hammer, pull the trigger, and ease the hammer down to the fired position. Insert a drift punch through the hole in the front of the hammer spring rod, move the rod toward the rear, and lift its head out of its seat in the back of the hammer. **Caution:** *The spring is under heavy tension, so control it as the rod and spring are eased out upward, and toward the left for removal.*

6. Take out the hammer pivot pin, and remove the hammer upward.

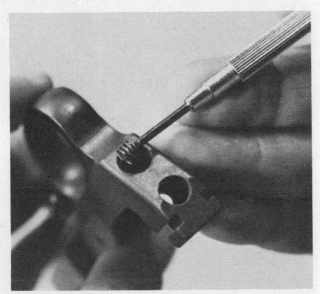

7. Insert a small tool at the rear of the trigger housing, and pull the trigger spring toward the rear until it stops, about as far as shown.

8. Restrain the sear, inside the trigger housing, and push out the trigger pin toward either side.

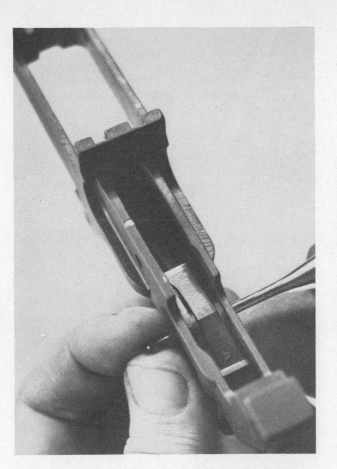

9. Remove the sear, sear spring, and trigger upward.

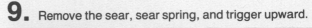

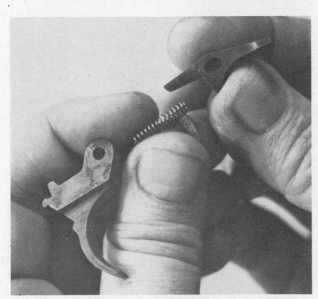

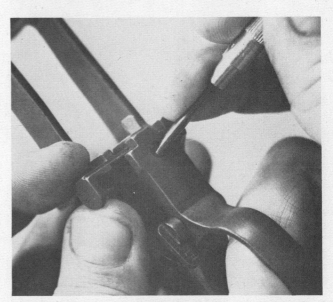

10. The sear and its spring are easily detached from the top of the trigger. After the trigger is removed, the trigger spring can be moved forward out of its well at the rear of the housing and taken out.

11. Insert a small screwdriver into the hole on the underside of the trigger housing, below the magazine catch, and push the catch retaining plunger toward the rear, holding it there while moving the catch out toward the right, along with its spring and plunger.

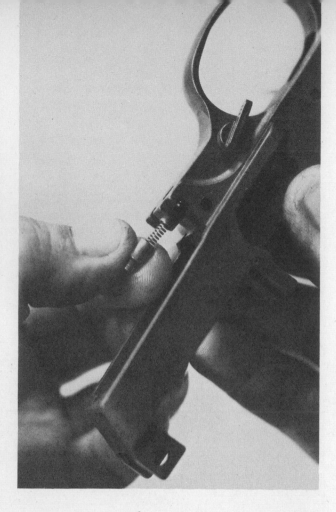

12. Remove the magazine catch retaining plunger toward the front, slowly releasing the tension of its spring. Remove the spring, and the rear plunger which positions the safety. The two plungers are identical, and need not be kept separated.

13. Remove the safety catch toward the right.

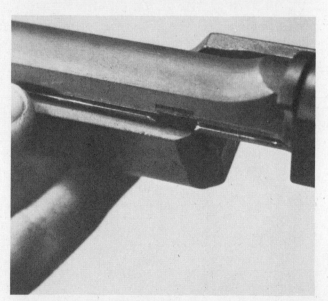

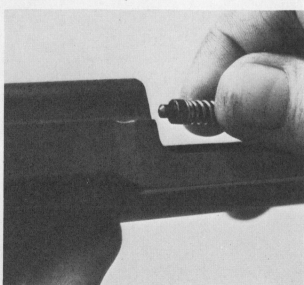

14. Grip the action slide spring and its guide rod firmly, just behind its front tip, and move it just far enough toward the rear to disengage its front stud from the recess on the back of the action slide. Tip the rod and spring away from the slide, and slowly ease the tension, removing them toward the front.

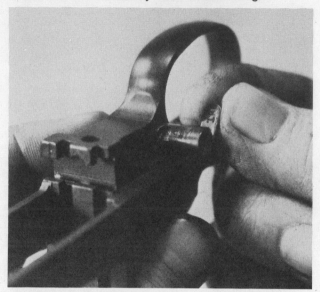

15. Move the action slide toward the rear until its inner projection on the left side is aligned with the exit cut in the barrel groove. Turn the slide toward the left and downward, disengaging the inner projection from the groove. At the same time, the rear lug of the cocking handle will be aligned with its exit cut in the receiver track, and the action slide can be removed.

16. Move the bolt to the position shown, and lift its right lug upward and toward the right. Rotate the bolt, and remove it upward and forward.

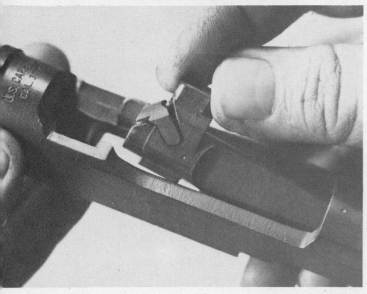

17. Dissassembly of the bolt is much easier if the special military tool is used. The knurled knob of the screw is turned to back it out, the bolt is laid in the tool, and the knob tightened, pushing the disassembly nose on the rotary piece against the extractor plunger. At the same time, the ejector is depressed by a post in the front of the tool. With these two parts held in place, the extractor is easily lifted out, the screw backed off, and the other parts removed. In the photo, the tool is shown with the screw tightened, ready for removal of the extractor. It is possible, without the tool, to use a small screwdriver to depress the extractor plunger. If this method is used, be sure to restrain the ejector, as it will be released when the extractor shaft clears its retaining cut.

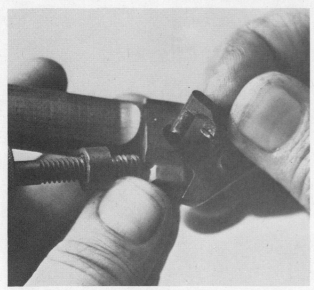

18. A hole is provided in the underside of the tool for pushing out the extractor, and it is removed upward.

19. After the extractor is removed, the screw on the tool is backed off, and the ejector and its spring are removed toward the front. The extractor plunger and its spring can be taken out of their hole at the base of the lug, and the firing pin can be removed from the rear of the bolt.

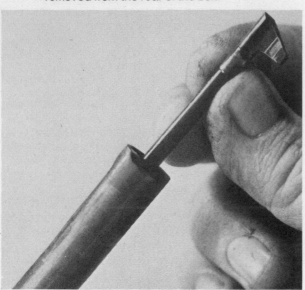

20. To remove the gas piston, it is best to use the standard military wrench designed for this. The retaining nut is simply unscrewed, and the piston is taken out toward the rear. It is possible to remove the nut without the wrench, with pliers, for example, but the nut is sure to be damaged.

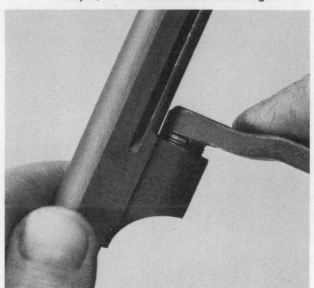

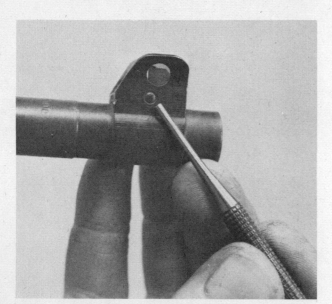

21. The front sight can be removed by drifting out its cross-pin, and using a non-marring punch to nudge it off toward the front. When the sight is taken off, be sure the small key inside it is not lost. The barrel band unit can be taken off after the sight is removed.

Reassembly Tips:

1. When replacing the ejector in the bolt, be sure the ejector is oriented as shown for proper engagement with the extractor post.

2. When replacing the tiny extractor plunger, be sure the notch on the plunger is oriented downward, as this surface locks the extractor in place.

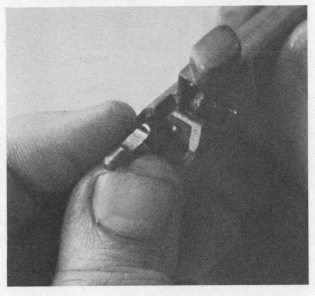

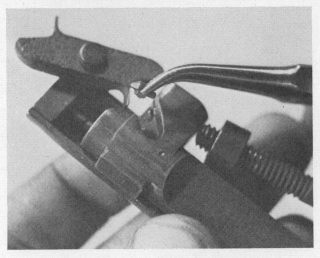

3. When properly assembled, the extractor and its plunger will be engaged as shown.

4. During replacement of the action slide, position the bolt as shown, then bring the slide onto the bolt lug and move it into place in its track.

Insert the trigger spring from the front, and push it back to the temporary rear position, just as in disassembly. After the trigger/sear system is installed, move the spring back toward the front, lifting its forward end to drop into the groove at the upper rear of the trigger.

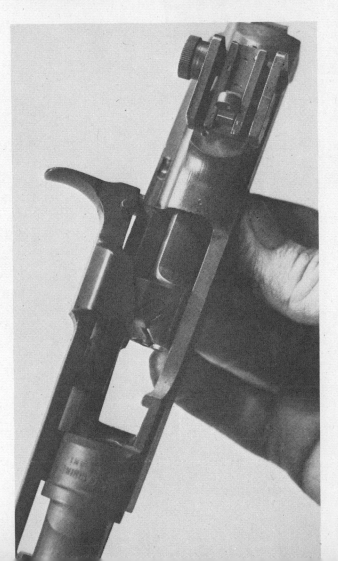

U.S. M-1 GARAND

Data: U.S. Garand (M1)
Origin: United States
Manufacturers: Springfield Armory, Winchester, and other contractors
Cartridge: 30-06 Springfield
Magazine capacity: 8 rounds
Over-all length: 43.6 inches
Barrel length: 24 inches
Weight: 9½ pounds

Although it may seem overweight and unwieldy in comparison with today's ultra-modern assault rifles and carbines. the old Garand was the finest military rifle of its day. It was adopted as U.S. military standard in 1936, and served us well through World War II and the Korean conflict. The trigger group mechanism is a particularly fine piece of engineering, and in slightly modified form lives on today in the Ruger Mini-14. The weakest point is the magazine system, where a complicated assortment of levers and arms somehow succeed in feeding the cartridges with excellent reliability.

Disassembly:

1. With the internal hammer cocked, the bolt closed, and the safety in the on-safe position, insert a rod or drift punch through the transverse hole at the rear of the trigger guard, and pull it toward the rear and outward, pivoting the guard downward and toward the front. Some late-production guns don't have a hole in the trigger guard, so simply pull toward the rear with the fingers or a non-marring tool.

2. Remove the trigger group downward. Push the buttstock downward, pivoting the receiver and barrel group upward at the rear, and remove the buttstock assembly.

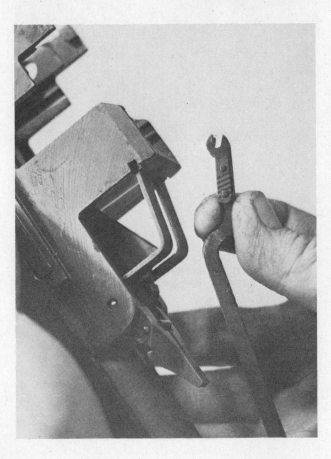

3. Grip the serrated surfaces on the sides of the rear tip of the follower rod, and move it forward, unhooking it from the follower arm. Slowly release the spring tension, and remove the follower rod and spring toward the rear.

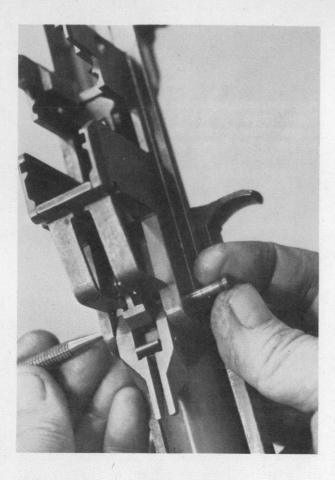

4. Remove the cross-pin that pivots the follower arm, pushing it out toward the right.

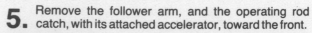

5. Remove the follower arm, and the operating rod catch, with its attached accelerator, toward the front.

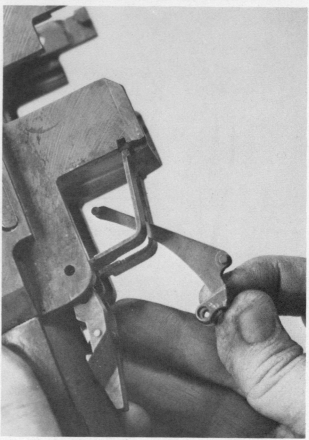

6. The accelerator is mounted in the operating rod catch by a cross-pin, and separating these parts is not recommended in normal disassembly.

7. Remove the cartridge guide from the front of the magazine housing.

8. Remove the follower assembly from the bottom of the magazine housing. Disassembly of the magazine follower is definitely not recommended.

10. Move the bolt back toward the front, until its front is about an inch from the rear of the barrel shroud, then remove it upward and toward the front, tilting it slightly toward the right.

9. Move the operating slide and bolt toward the rear until the lug on the inside of the handle is aligned with the exit cut in the slide track. Push the handle upward, then out toward the left, and turn the slide for removal toward the rear.

11. When disassembling the bolt, a Garand tool is helpful, but not absolutely necessary. It is not difficult to depress the extractor plunger with a small screwdriver while lifting the extractor out of its recess upward. **Caution:** *The ejector will be released as soon as the extractor post clears its retaining cut, and the ejector spring is quite strong, so control it and ease it out.*

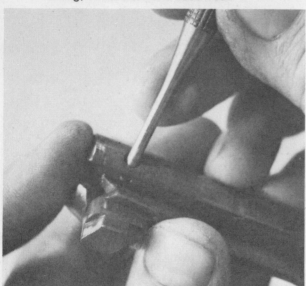

12. Remove the firing pin from the rear of the bolt.

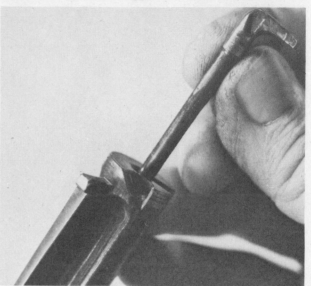

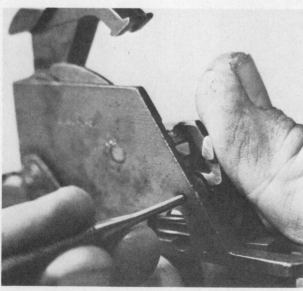

13. Snap the trigger guard back into place, release the safety, restrain the hammer, and pull the trigger. Lower the hammer to the fired position. Exert pressure on the rear of the sear, to slightly compress the hammer spring and relieve tension on the trigger pin, and drift out the trigger pin toward the right. **Caution:** *The hammer spring is quite strong, so keep firm pressure on the back of the sear.*

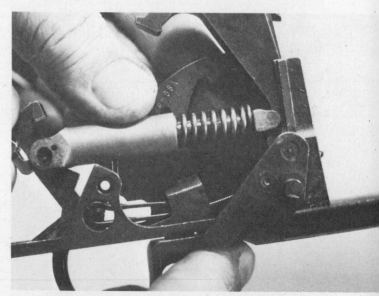

14. Slowly release the spring tension, allowing the trigger/sear assembly and the hammer spring housing to move upward and toward the rear. Control the hammer spring housing with downward pressure, as it will tend to climb out.

15. Remove the hammer spring housing, the spring, and the hammer strut upward and toward the rear. Remove the trigger/sear assembly upward. The sear is cross-pin mounted on the trigger, but these parts should not be separated in normal disassembly.

16. Push out the hammer pivot pin toward the right.

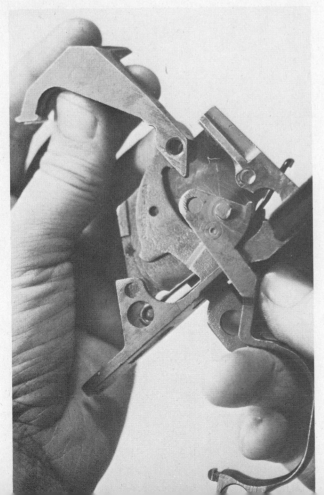

18. Move the safety to the off-safe position, and tilt its upper arm toward the right, until its pivot-post moves out of its hole in the housing, then remove it upward.

17. Move the trigger guard toward the rear. Move the hammer toward the rear, then remove it upward and toward the right.

19. Move the trigger guard toward the rear until its right upper arm is aligned with the open space in the housing, and tilt the right arm inward (toward the left), removing the guard downward and toward the right.

20. Use a drift punch to tap the clip ejector spring off its post, working through the access hole in the left wall of the trigger group. The spring can also be simply pried off the post from inside, using a screwdriver blade.

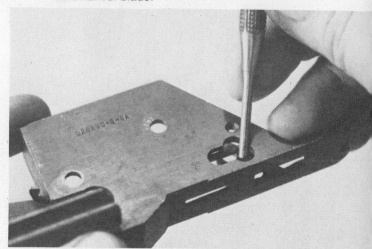

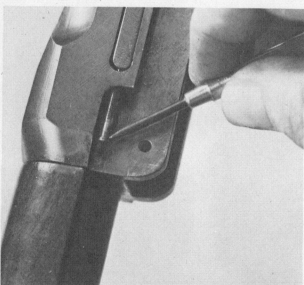

21. Use a drift punch to start the clip latch pin out toward the front, until its larger front tip can be grasped or pushed with a screwdriver blade, and pull the pin toward the front and out. The latch and its spring are then taken off toward the left.

22. Unscrew the gas piston nut, located below the barrel at the muzzle, and remove it.

23. Unscrew the gas cylinder lock, and take it off toward the front.

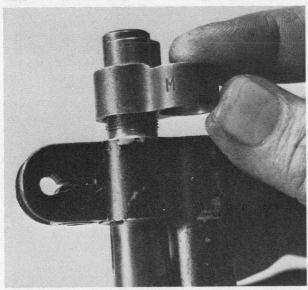

24. Slide the gas cylinder off toward the front. If it is very tight, tap it with a plastic hammer to free it.

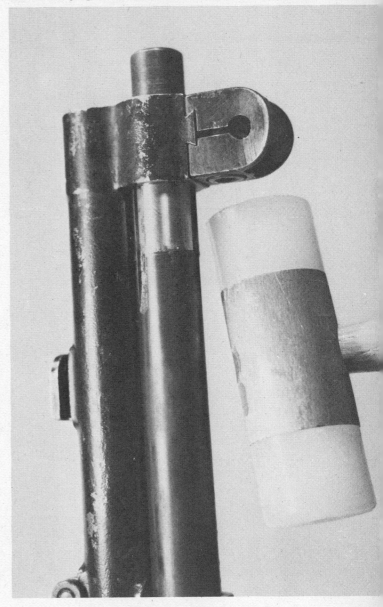

25. Remove the front handguard wood toward the front. Drift out the cross-pin in the underside of the rear band, and remove the band toward the front.

26. Snap the rear upper handguard band out of its grooves in the barrel, and remove the handguard.

Reassembly Tips:

1. When replacing the ejector and its spring, be sure the recess on the ejector is properly oriented for engagement with the extractor post. When replacing the extractor, press the front face of the bolt against a hard surface to keep the ejector depressed while inserting the extractor. The extractor has a camming surface beside the plunger, and can just be snapped into place, without depressing the plunger manually.

When replacing the operating slide latch, be sure the hook at its rear engages the *top* of the inner projection of the clip latch.

When replacing the magazine follower arm, be sure its rear side studs enter the track on the underside of the follower before inserting the cross-pin.

When attaching the follower rod hooks to the studs on the follower arm, depress the carrier slightly to allow them to snap into place.

U.S. 1903 SPRINGFIELD

Data:	U.S. 1903 Springfield
Origin:	United States
Manufacturer:	Springfield Arsenal and Rock Island Armory
Cartridge:	30-06 Springfield
Magazine capacity:	5 rounds
Over-all length:	43.2 inches
Barrel length:	24 inches
Weight:	8.6 pounds

Adopted by the U.S. as military standard in 1903, this rifle replaced the Krag-Jorgensen, and was used until the adoption of the M1 Garand in 1936. Although officially replaced, the Springfield saw quite a bit of use during World War II. In 1942, the Remington Arms Company did a slight re-design of the gun, mostly to make it easier to manufacture, and this rifle was designated the Model 1903A3. The main differences were in the use of stamped-steel parts to replace several of the machined parts of the original gun, such as the magazine floorplate, and the rear sight was moved to the rear of the receiver. Mechanically, they are essentially the same.

Disassembly:

1. Cycle the bolt to cock the striker, and set the safety lever in the vertical position. Set the magazine cutoff lever, located at the left rear of the receiver, at its mid-position, angled slightly upward from the horizontal. Remove the bolt toward the rear.

2. Depress the bolt sleeve lock (arrow), located on the left side, and unscrew the sleeve and striker assembly counter-clockwise (rear view). Remove the sleeve and striker assembly toward the rear, taking care not to trip the safety lever.

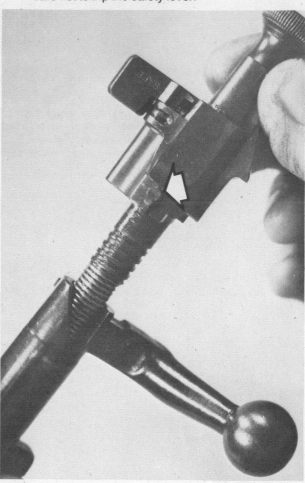

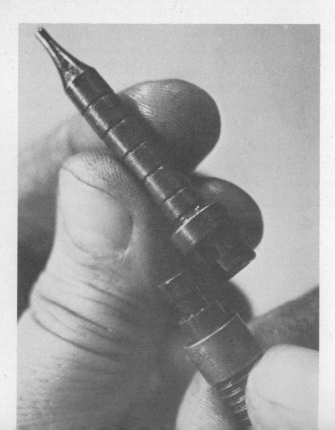

3. Holding firmly to the sleeve and striker knob, turn the safety back to the off-safe position and allow the striker to move forward in the sleeve. Grip the serrated area on the retaining sleeve, just to the rear of the firing pin, and pull the sleeve toward the rear until it clears the back of the firing pin. Remove the firing pin toward the side. **Caution:** *Rest the striker knob on a firm surface during this operation, and keep a firm grip on the firing pin retaining sleeve, as the striker spring is quite strong.*

4. Slowly release the spring tension, and remove the retaining sleeve and the spring toward the front.

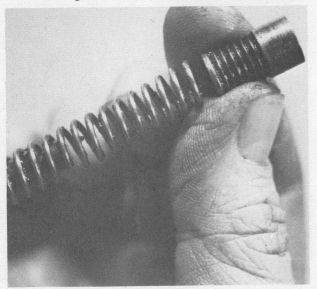

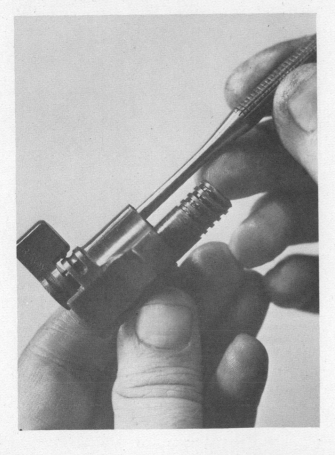

5. Slide the bolt sleeve off the striker rod toward the front.

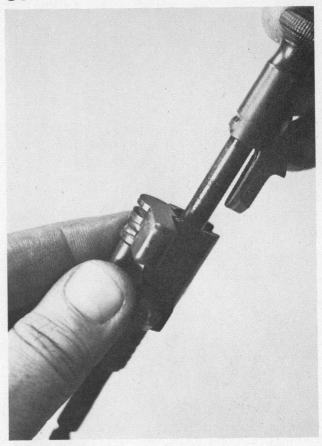

6. Turn the safety lever back to its mid-position and rest the lower rear edge of the bolt sleeve on a firm surface. Use a drift punch against the front tip of the safety shaft to drive it out toward the rear. Note that the safety plunger and spring will be released as the safety clears the rear of the bolt sleeve, so ease them out and take care that they are not lost.

7. Turn the extractor clockwise (rear view) until its front underlug is out of the groove at the front of the bolt, and is aligned with the un-grooved area on the bolt. Push the extractor forward and off its T-mount on the bolt ring.

8. Insert a drift punch in the hole on the underside, just forward of the trigger guard, and depress the magazine floorplate latch. Move the floorplate toward the rear. Remove the floorplate and the attached spring and follower downward. The spring is easily detached from the floorplate and follower.

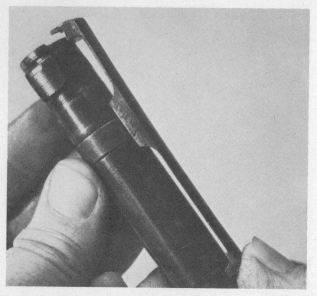

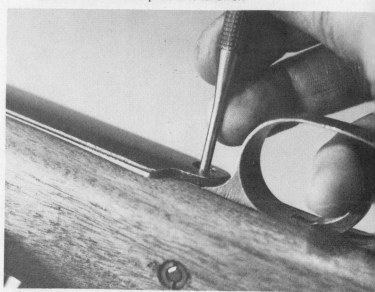

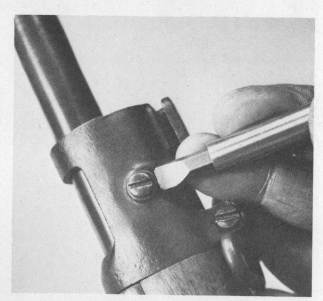

9. Remove the cross-screw in the front barrel band, and slide the barrel band forward.

10. Depress the lock spring on the right side, in front of the rear barrel band (after the band screw and sling loop are removed), and slide the band off toward the front. Move the upper handguard wood forward, and take it off.

11. Remove the large vertical screws on the underside at the front and rear of the magazine/trigger guard unit. Remove the action from the stock, and take off the trigger guard unit downward.

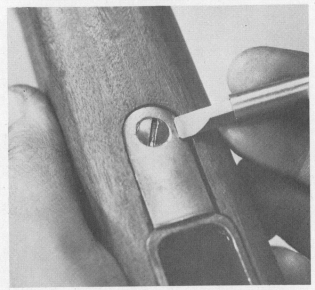

12. The ejector is retained on the left side of the receiver by a vertical pin with a slotted screw-type head at its lower end. If the pin is unusually tight, using a screwdriver to turn it will help to loosen it, but for removal it is driven out downward. The ejector is taken out toward the inside of the receiver.

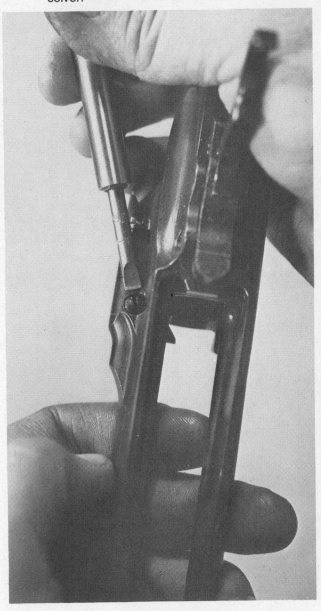

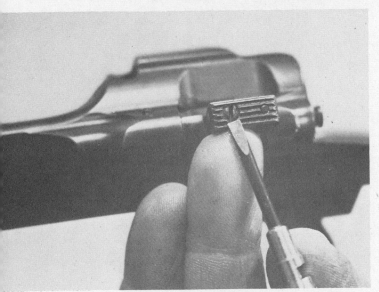

13. Remove the small screw in the serrated end of the bolt stop/magazine cutoff lever.

14. The bolt stop pivot has a cannelure at its rear tip, allowing it to be pulled out with a fingernail or a screwdriver blade. When removing the pivot pin, keep slight inward pressure on the bolt stop, to relieve spring pressure on the pin.

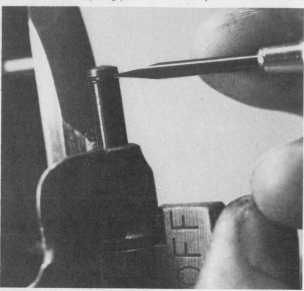

15. Remove the bolt stop/magazine cutoff toward the left, taking care not to lose the positioning plunger and its spring.

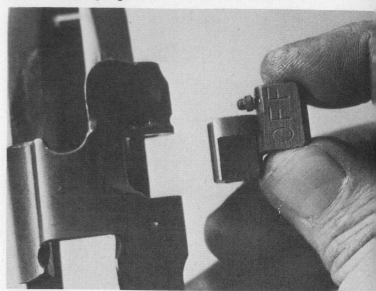

16. Push out the sear pivot pin toward the left. As soon as its large head clears its recess in the underside of the receiver, exert slight pressure on the front of the sear to compress the spring and assist withdrawal of the pin.

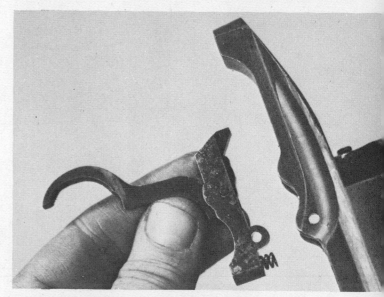

17. Remove the trigger, sear, and sear spring assembly downward. Drifting out the trigger cross-pin will allow separation of the trigger from the sear.

Reassembly Tips:

18. To take the front barrel band completely off, the front sight must be drifted out of its dovetail to allow the band to pass. The front sight blade is retained in the dovetailed base by a cross-pin.

1. When replacing the safety lever in the bolt sleeve, insert a small screwdriver to depress the positioning plunger and spring, and note that the lever should be in its midway (vertical) position for installation.

Before the bolt is replaced in the receiver, the striker must be in the cocked position, with the bolt handle raised. Since the Springfield has a cocking knob, this is easily done.

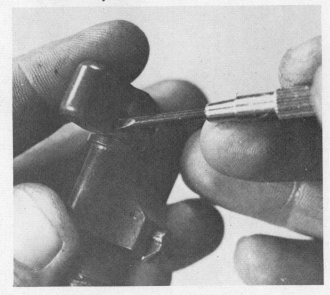

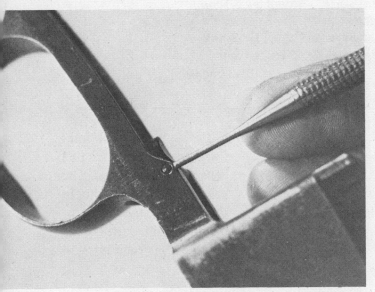

19. Drifting out the cross-pin in the trigger guard unit will allow removal of the magazine floorplate latch and its spring upward. The spring is quite strong, so control it and ease it out.

WEATHERBY MARK V

Data:	Weatherby Mark V
Origin:	United States
Manufacturer:	Weatherby, South Gate, California (actions imported, some made by Sauer)
Cartridges:	A long list of standard and Weatherby Magnum calibers
Magazine capacity:	2 to 5 rounds
Over-all length:	43¼ to 46½ inches
Barrel length:	24 or 26 inches
Weight:	6½ to 10½ pounds

From the first Weatherby rifle in 1948 to the present time, Roy's guns have established a standard of excellence that is rivalled only by the more expensive custom rifles. The Mark V, first offered in 1955, is still in production. In 1970 a lower-priced version, the Vanguard, was introduced, and it shares many of the mechanical features of the Mark V. With some exceptions, these instructions will generally apply to the Vanguard as well.

Disassembly:

1. Open the bolt, hold the trigger pulled to the rear, and remove the bolt from the rear of the receiver.

2. Grip the underlug of the cocking piece firmly with smooth-jawed non-marring pliers, and move the cocking piece toward the rear until it can be turned to engage its front step on the inside of the bolt sleeve. This will lock the striker in rear position, as shown.

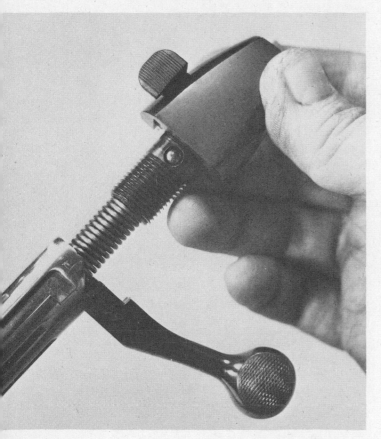

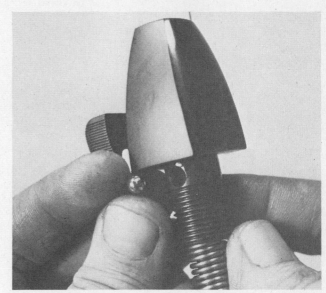

4. Remove the lock ball from its well on top of the bolt sleeve neck, and take care that it isn't lost.

3. Unscrew the bolt from the sleeve and striker assembly, and remove it toward the front. Keep the sleeve in the upright position during this operation, as the firing pin lock ball will be freed from its hole at the front of the sleeve as soon as it clears the rear of the bolt.

5. Turn the cocking piece out of its lock step inside the bolt sleeve, and allow it to move forward into its recess on the underside of the sleeve.

6. Note that the base of the firing pin at the front of the striker shaft (not shown) has flat sides. Grip the bolt sleeve firmly, and by hand or with parallel-jaw pliers unscrew the striker shaft from the cocking piece. Keep frontward pressure on the sleeve, as the striker spring is partially compressed. Ease the spring tension slowly, and remove the striker and spring toward the front.

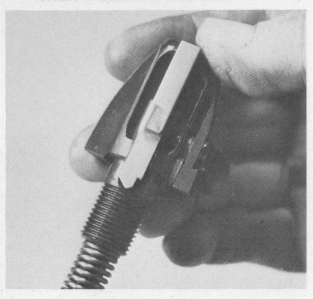

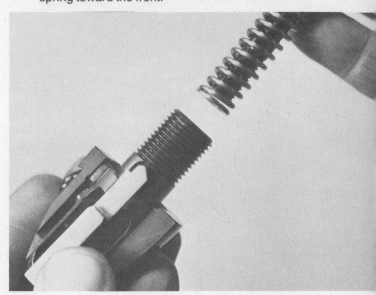

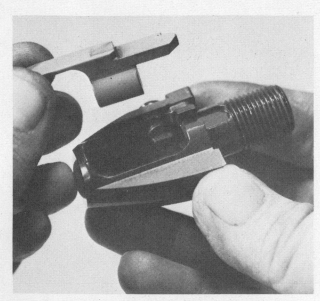

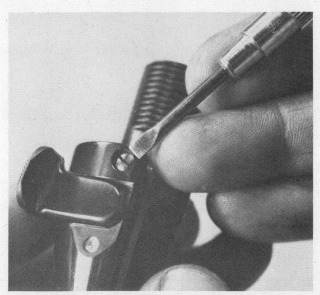

7. Remove the cocking piece from the bolt sleeve.

8. The safety is retained in the bolt sleeve by its positioning lever and spring, and the lever is held by a screw on the right side. Remove the screw, and take out the lever and spring toward the front. The safety is then removed toward the right.

9. The ejector is retained by a cross-pin at the front of the bolt. **Caution:** *The ejector spring is under tension. Control the ejector and ease it out toward the front.*

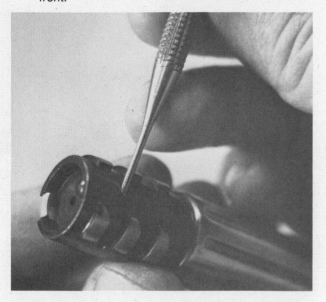

10. The extractor is also retained by a cross-pin on the right side at the front of the bolt. Drifting out the pin will free the extractor and its coil spring for removal.

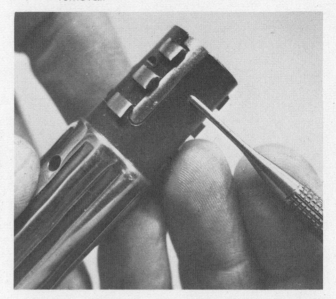

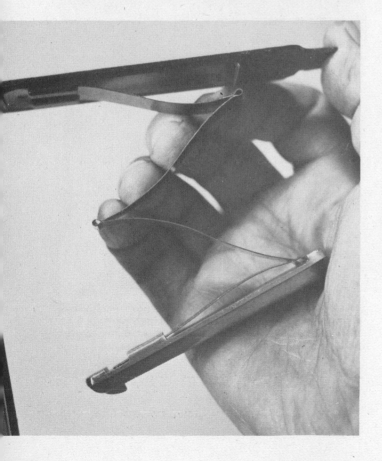

12. Close the floorplate, and remove the large vertical screw at the front of the magazine plate. Remove the large vertical screw at the rear of the trigger guard, and take off the trigger guard assembly downward. Separate the action from the stock.

11. Operate the latch and open the magazine floorplate. Slide the magazine spring out of its slots inside the floorplate. The follower is separated from the spring in the same way.

13. Drifting out the cross-pin will allow the magazine floorplate to be removed.

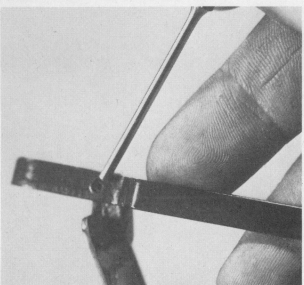

14. Drifting out the roll pin that retains the floorplate latch will allow removal of the latch and its spring downward and toward the front.

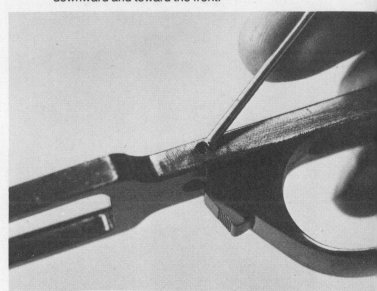

15. When the action is taken out of the stock, the magazine box will be released for removal. Note that there is a spacer plate (in some calibers) at the rear of the box, and take care that it isn't overlooked and lost.

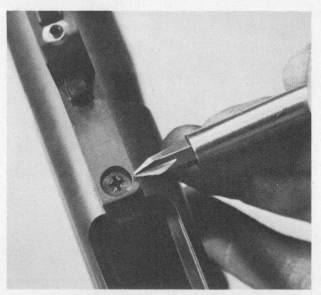

16. On earlier guns, the trigger housing is retained by a post and cross-pin. On the late model shown, two Phillips-head screws hold the housing to the underside of the receiver. One screw enters from below, at the front of the housing, and the other enters from above, located in the floor of the bolt track at the rear. Taking out these screws will allow removal of the housing downward, but this will not be necessary in normal disassembly.

18. The angle of the trigger "shoe" on its lower extension is adjustable by means of a tiny screw on the left side. The shoe can be removed by drifting out its cross-pin.

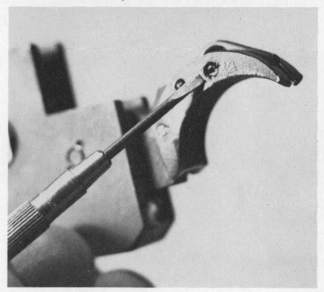

17. Early Mark V rifles had a trigger housing with a removable sideplate. Note that on this late gun, the housing is a one-piece casting, and the trigger and sear cross-pins are heavily staked in place to discourage disassembly. If necessary, the pins can be removed. The trigger is taken out toward the rear and downward, the sear upward, and the bolt stop upward (after removal of the trigger). Unless something needs repair, it's best to leave these parts in place.

Disassembly:

1. When replacing the magazine box, in those calibers which have a spacer plate at the rear, note that the plate is inserted from below, with its "shelf" turned toward the rear, to seal off the excess space.

2. When replacing the striker, turning its threaded rear tip back into the cocking piece, note that the striker shaft has recesses on its side which align with the lock ball in the neck of the sleeve. Also, note that the depth to which the shaft is turned controls the degree of protrusion of the firing pin point at the bolt face.

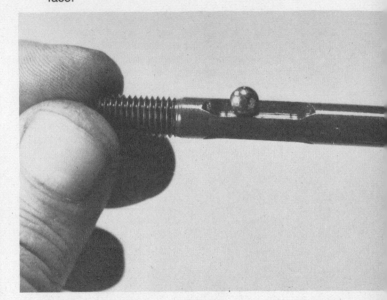

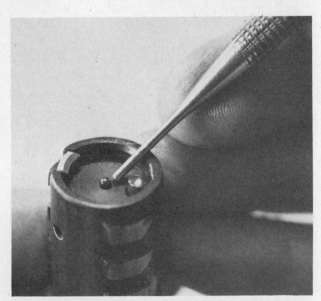

3. When the striker and bolt sleeve system is fully assembled and installed in the bolt, let the striker move forward to the fired position, and check the degree of firing pin point protrusion at the bolt face. If it is more than the one shown, it must be adjusted. Note that the striker must be re-cocked before the bolt is put back into the receiver.

WINCHESTER MODEL 70

Data:	Winchester Model 70
Origin:	United States
Manufacturer:	Winchester Repeating Arms Company New Haven, Connecticut
Cartridges:	From 222 to 458, including several magnum rounds
Magazine capacity:	Varies with cartridges
Over-all length:	42½ to 44½ inches
Barrel length:	22 and 24 inches
Weight:	About 7½ pounds

The original Model 70 first appeared in 1936, and was made until 1963. An "economy" version was made between 1964 and 1972, and since that time the original quality was resumed, with some of the innovations of the 1964 version retained. Collectors, and some shooters, treasure the pre-1964 "originals," but in some ways, the later guns, as now currently made, are mechanically superior. A list of the calibers and model variations of the Model 70 would nearly fill an entire page. The gun covered here is a late standard model. On the pre-1964 guns, the bolt detail is quite similar to the standard Mauser pattern.

Disassembly:

1. To remove the bolt, the safety must be in the off-safe position. Open the bolt, and depress the bolt stop, located at the left rear of the receiver. Hold it down, and withdraw the bolt toward the rear. For clarity, the bolt stop is indicated with a drift punch in the photo. It is depressed with a fingertip.

2. Remove the screws on the underside at the front and rear of the trigger guard. Note that on some Model 70 guns the magazine is a through-type, with a hinged cover-plate. The one shown in the photos is a closed type, with a solid stock underside. After the guard screws are removed, the guard can be taken off downward.

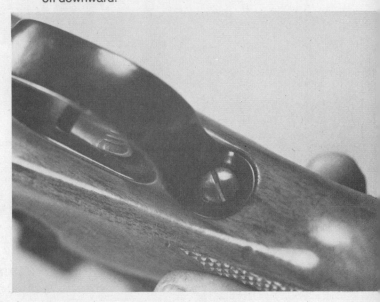

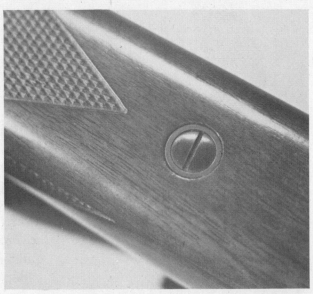

3. Remove the main stock mounting screw, on the underside below the chamber area. If the gun is a through-magazine type, this screw will be in the forward base of the magazine floorplate. When all three screws are removed, the action can be taken out of the stock.

4. If the gun is a blind-magazine type, the magazine follower, spring, and internal floorplate can be taken out upward. If the gun has an external floorplate, the floorplate and front hinge plate can be taken off downward. The plate is attached to its base with a cross-pin. A cross-pin also retains the floorplate catch and its spring in the front of the trigger guard.

5. The magazine box, or housing, is usually a tight press fit on the bottom of the receiver, and can be removed by exerting downward pressure while working it gently from side to side.

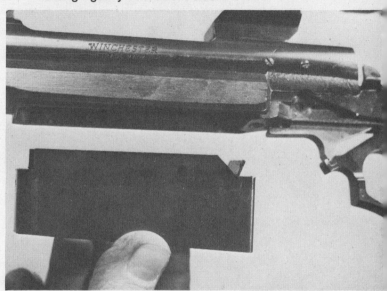

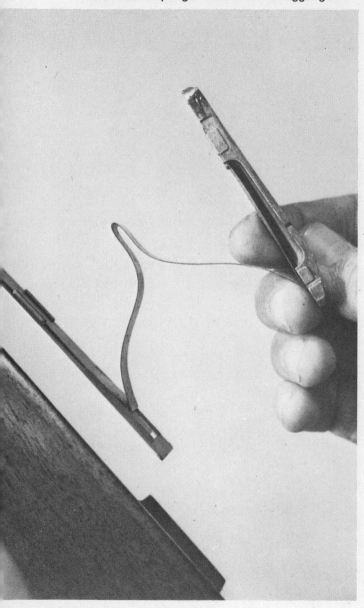

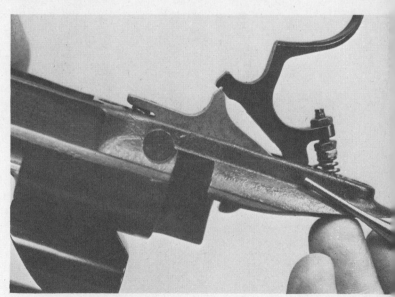

6. A cross-pin retains the trigger assembly on the underside of the receiver. Note that the trigger, its spring, and adjustment system can be removed downward without disturbing the adjustment. The cross-pin must be drifted out toward the left.

7. Note that the trigger pin has an enlarged head on the left side, and is also the pivot and retainer for the bolt stop and its spring. Before removal, note the relationship of the bolt stop, its spring, and the trigger, to aid reassembly. Restrain the spring as the pin is drifted out, and ease it off.

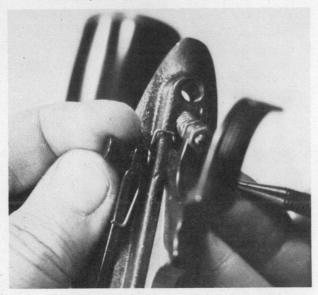

8. The bolt stop is moved downward and toward the rear for removal.

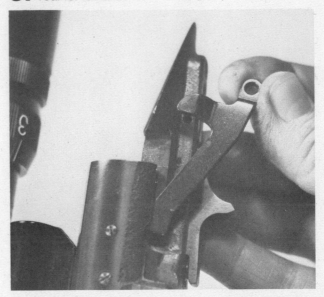

9. The sear is retained on the underside of the receiver by a cross-pin which must be drifted out toward the right. Restrain the sear against the tension of its strong spring, and remove the sear and spring downward.

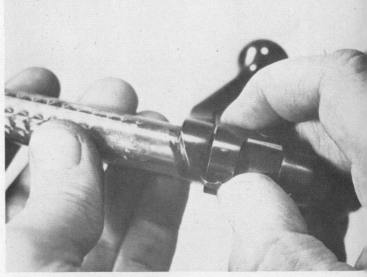

10. Grip the lower lug of the cocking piece firmly in a vise, and move the bolt forward until the safety can be turned back to the safe position. Depress the bolt sleeve lock plunger, located on the left side of the bolt, and unscrew the rear section, the bolt sleeve. During this operation, take care that the safety is not tripped to the fire position.

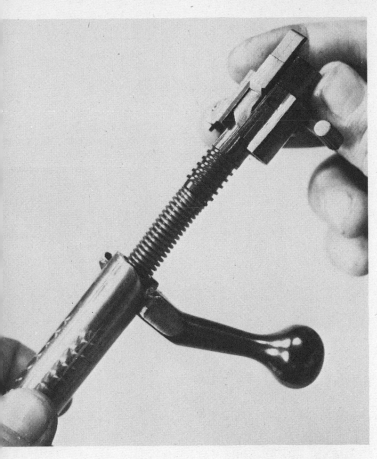

11. When the sleeve and striker assembly has cleared its internal threads, withdraw it toward the rear.

12. Grip the forward portion of the striker firmly in a vise, with the spring retaining C-clip and compression washer just above the vise jaws. Pry the compression washer upward, remove the C-clip, and allow the washer and spring to come down on the vise. With a firm hold on the bolt sleeve, open the vise, and slowly ease the assembly upward, releasing the tension of the spring. Take care not to lose the compression washer. If the gun is an older one, spring removal is done by simply pulling the firing pin sleeve slightly toward the rear, giving it a quarter-turn in either direction, and easing it off toward the front. After the tension is relieved, take off the spring toward the front.

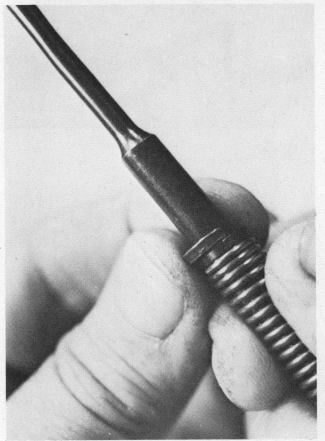

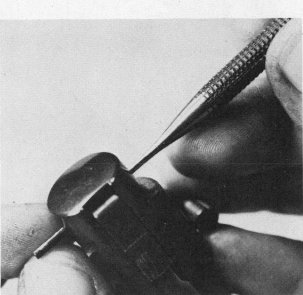

13. Drift out the cross-pin in the bolt end-piece, at the rear of the bolt sleeve.
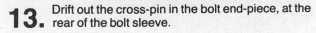

14. Remove the bolt end-piece toward the rear. If it is tight, it can be tapped off by sliding the striker assembly against it.

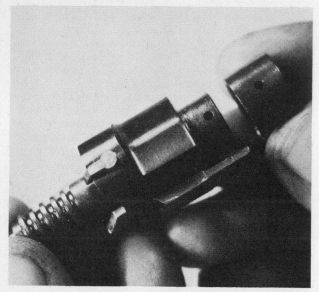

15. Remove the striker assembly from the rear of the bolt sleeve.

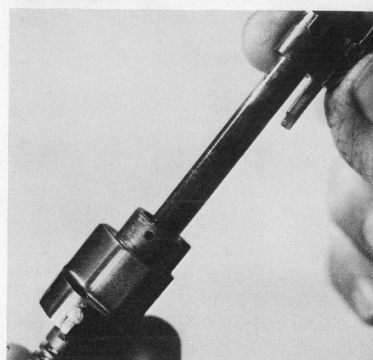

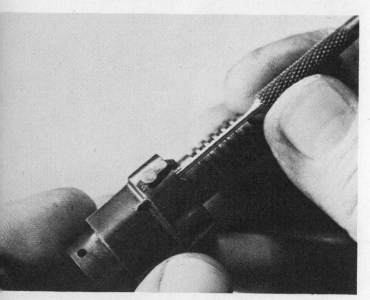

16. To remove the bolt sleeve lock plunger and spring, push out the retaining pin, which runs lengthwise in the sleeve, and take off the plunger and spring toward the side.

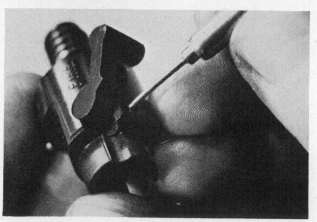

17. Use a very small drift punch to push the small pin beside the safety inward, into the interior of the bolt sleeve. The safety lever should be in the off-safe position.

18. Turn the safety around toward the rear, then move it upward and out of the bolt sleeve. **Caution:** *The safety positioning spring and plunger will be released as the safety clears the sleeve, so restrain them and ease them out.*

19. To remove the ejector, drift out the angled cross-pin at the front of the bolt. **Caution;** *The strong ejector spring will expel the ejector as the drift is removed, so ease the ejector out toward the front, and remove the spring.*

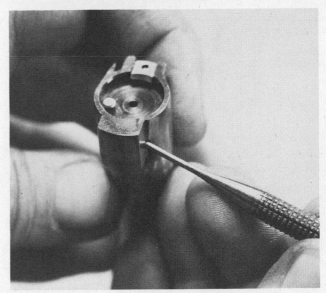

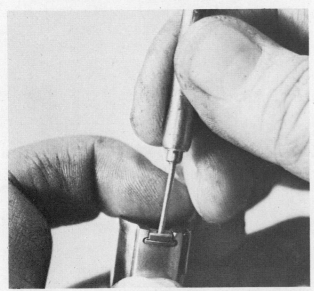

20. To remove the extractor, use a small-diameter drift punch to depress the extractor plunger, accessible through a small hole in the front face of the extractor. While keeping the plunger depressed, move the extractor out of its T-slot in the bolt lug. **Caution:** *Restrain the plunger and spring, and ease them out.* If the gun is an older one, it will have a long external Mauser-style extractor. For removal details on this type, see the Mauser or Springfield section.

Reassembly Tips:

1. When replacing the striker spring, note that the retaining C-clip has a recess on one side. This side must go toward the front. With the forward part of the striker gripped in a vise (as in disassembly), this means that the recess on the C-clip should be installed downward, toward the vise jaws.

2. Before the bolt sleeve and striker assembly can be reinstalled in the bolt body, the striker must be locked to the rear by placing the safety in the on-safe position. Grip the lower lug of the striker firmly in a vise, push the bolt sleeve toward the front, and set the safety. When the sleeve and striker assembly are back in the bolt body, the safety must be released to the off-safe position before the bolt can be re-inserted in the receiver.

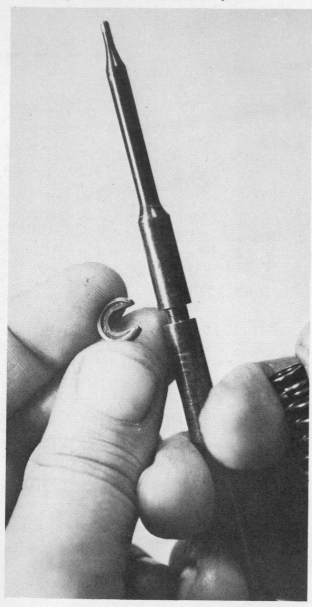

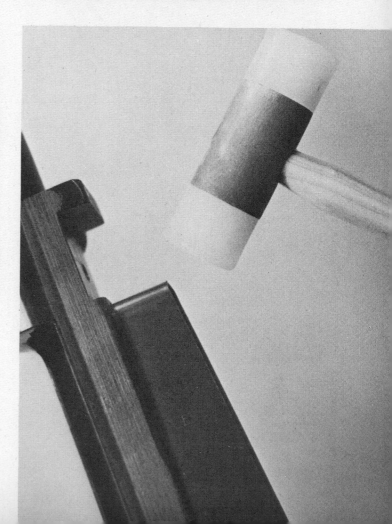

3. If the magazine housing has been removed, insert its rear edge into the recess first, then tap the front gently inward and toward the rear until it is in place.

WINCHESTER MODEL 71

Data: Winchester Model 71
Origin: United States
Manufacturer: Winchester Repeating Arms
New Haven, Connecticut
Cartridge: 348 Winchester
Magazine capacity: 4 rounds
Over-all length: 40 and 42 inches
Barrel length: 20 and 24 inches
Weight: 8 pounds

When production of the venerable Model 1886 ended in 1937, it had already been replaced (a year earlier) in the Winchester line by the excellent Model 71. This gun had all the best features of the Model 1886, and was chambered for a new cartridge, the 348 Winchester. The rifle was discontinued in 1958, but it was very poular in the north country, and many are still in use. Although it externally resembles the other lever-action Winchesters, its internal mechanism is quite different, as the takedown sequence will show.

Disassembly:

1. Remove the large vertical screw at the rear tip of the upper tang, and take off the buttstock toward the rear. If it is very tight, bump the front of the comb with the heel of the hand to start it.

2. With the hammer in the fired position, drift out the cross-pin in the lower tang that retains the hammer spring base. **Caution:** *The powerful hammer spring is under some tension, even when at rest. Control the spring base, and ease it toward the rear. Take out the base, and the hammer spring, toward the rear.*

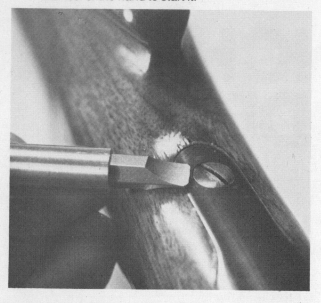

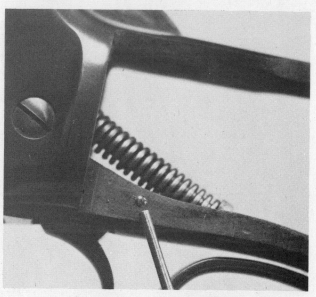

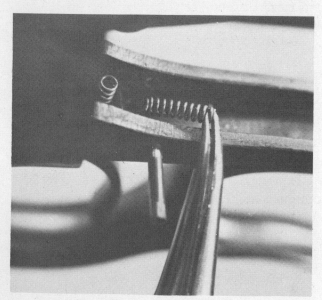

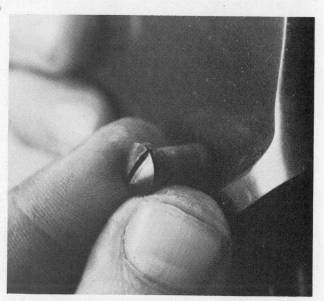

3. When the spring base is removed, the small coil spring that powers the trigger block safety will be freed for removal from the left side beneath the base. Note that this spring, and the trigger block safety, are not found on all Model 71 rifles. At this point, the trigger spring can also be removed from the upper rear of the trigger.

4. Remove the hammer screw toward the left.

5. Remove the hammer screw bushing toward the left. If the bushing is tight, there is a small hole inside it to give lodging for a drift point, inserted from the opposite side, to nudge it out.

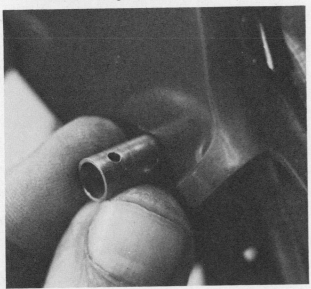

6. Slide the lower tang toward the rear, and remove it. The lever can be partially opened during this operation, for clearance of the trigger.

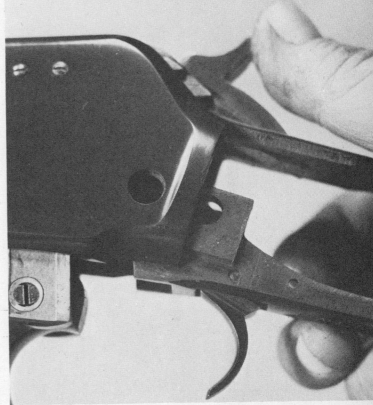

7. Remove the hammer and the attached hammer strut downward.

8. Drifting out the cross-pin in the lower tang will allow removal of the trigger and sear from the tang. If the trigger block safety is present, taking out the trigger will also free it for removal.

9. Drift out the lever bushing pin toward the right. Note that the left tip of this pin may have the look of a screw slot, but it is actually a split tempered pin which locks the lever pivot bushing.

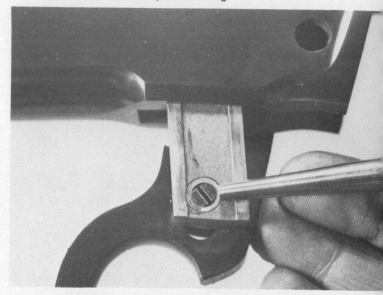

10. Remove the lever pivot bushing toward the left.

11. Remove the left locking block downward. The right locking block is not removed at this time.

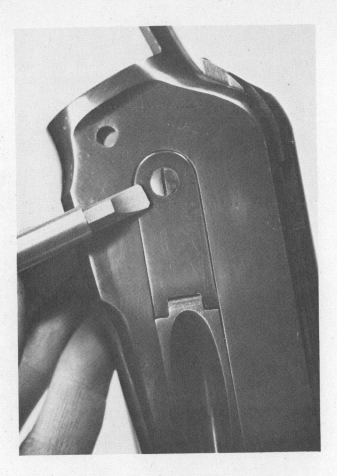

12. Remove the loading gate base screw, on the right side of the receiver, and take off the loading gate assembly toward the right. The gate spring can be removed from its recess on the inside of the base, and drifting out the hinge pin will allow separation of the gate from the base.

13. With the bolt pushed back to the front, and the right locking block pushed partially into place to lock it, align the recess on the front of the locking block with the rear tip of the cartridge guide. Remove the cartridge guide screw, and move the cartridge guide toward the rear to free it from its recess.

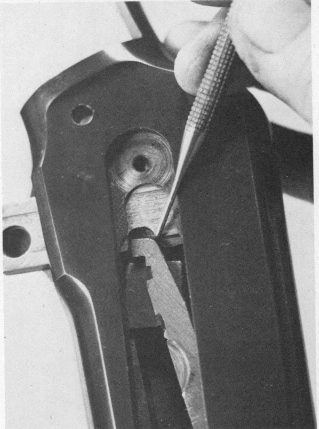

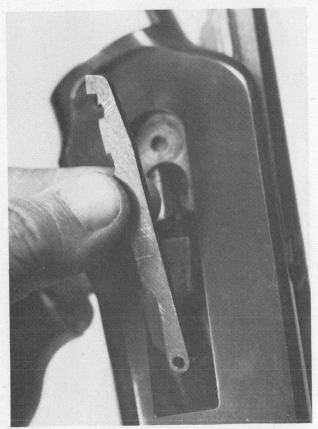

14. Open the bolt, and tip the front end of the cartridge guide inward. Remove the guide from the receiver opening.

15. The right locking block can now be removed downward.

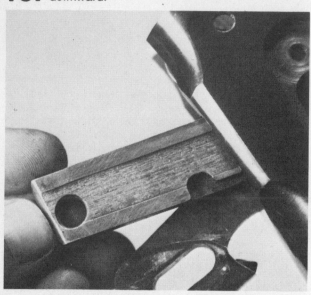

16. Move the bolt all the way to the rear, out of its tracks in the receiver, and tilt the assembly to clear the carrier. Remove the carrier downward. The carrier plunger and spring can be removed by drifting out the pin at the rear of the carrier.

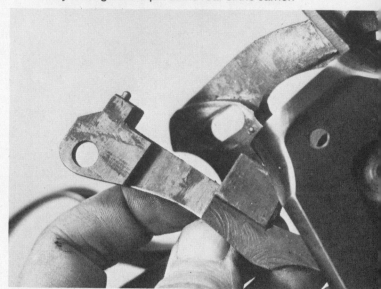

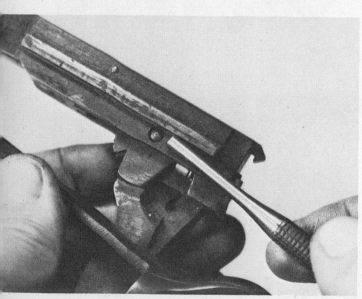

17. Drift out the lever link pin, and separate the lever from the bolt. **Caution:** *This will also release the ejector and its spring and collar, so control them and ease them out.*

18. Remove the lever downward. The lever latch plunger and its spring are retained in the lever by a cross-pin. Control the plunger, and ease it out.

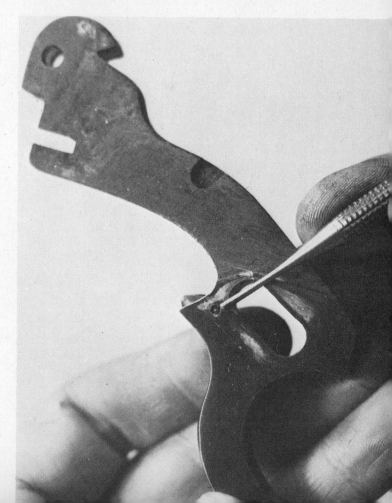
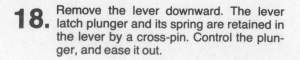

19. When removing the ejector from the front of the bolt, take care not to lose the small collar at the rear of the ejector spring.

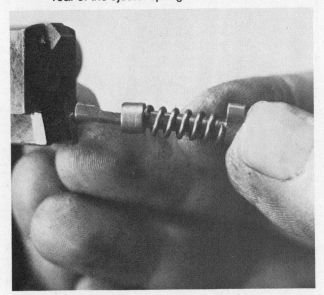

20. Drifting out the cross-pin at the lower rear of the bolt will allow removal of the firing pin toward the rear.

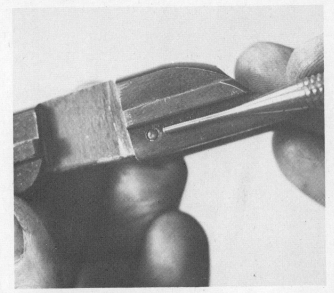

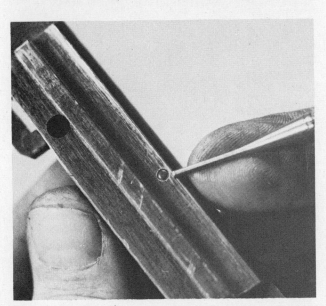

21. Drifting out the cross-pin at top center will allow removal of the extractor. Don't lift the extractor upward. Hook a tool under its beak at the front, and lever it out forward.

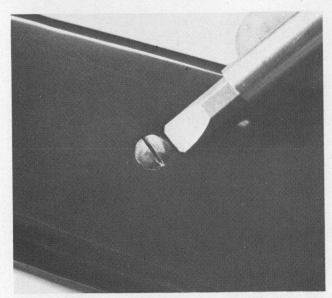

22. Remove the large screw on the left side of the receiver, and take out the cartridge stop from inside the receiver.

23. Remove the screw on the underside, near the front end of the magazine tube, and take out the endpiece toward the front. **Caution:** *The magazine spring is partially compressed, so control it and ease it out.* Remove the spring and follower toward the front.

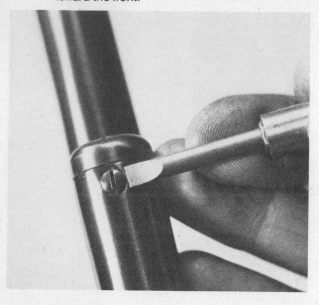

24. Remove the screws on each side of the fore-end tip, and slide the tip off toward the front.

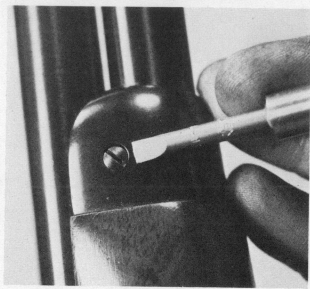

25. Insert a drift punch through the screw holes in the end of the magazine tube, and unscrew the tube counter-clockwise (front view). Remove the tube toward the front. Drift the fore-end tip tenon out of its dovetail toward the right, and move the fore-end forward and off.

Reassembly Tips:

1. Before replacing the hammer bushing and screw, insert a tapered drift punch to align the hammer, carrier, and lower tang loops.

2. Replacement of the hammer spring system will be easier if a slave pin is used, as shown, to restrain the spring during installation. If the trigger block safety is present, install the hammer spring system, then insert the safety spring through the opening in the base, compressing it to snap it into place.

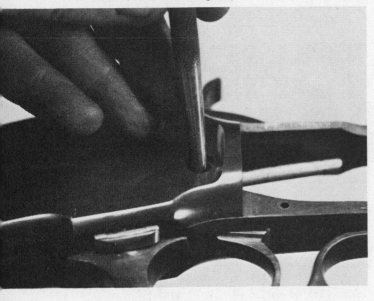

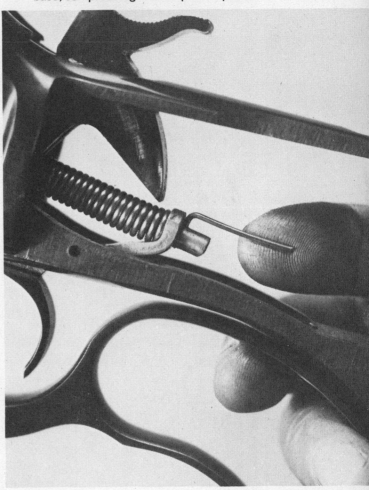

WINCHESTER MODEL 1892

Data:	Winchester Model 1892
Origin:	United States
Manufacturer:	Winchester Repeating Arms Company New Haven, Connecticut
Cartridges:	44-40, 38-40, 32-20, and 25-20
Magazine capacity:	14 rounds (rifle), 12 rounds (carbine)
Over-all length:	41¾ inches (rifle)
Barrel length:	24 inches (rifle), 20 inches (carbine)
Weight:	6¾ pounds (rifle)

Another of John M. Browning's masterpieces for Winchester, the Model 1892 was made in rifle form until 1932, and in carbine style until 1941. Slim, elegant, and totally reliable, the Model 92 was popular for many reasons, one of which was its chambering for the same cartridges as the Colt revolver in its three larger calibers. In today's market, collectors and shooters vie for the few remaining guns in circulation. I know of several of these guns that are still in regular use as small to medium-size game rifles.

Disassembly:

1. Remove the vertical stock mounting screw, located at the rear of the upper tang, and take off the stock toward the rear. If it's tight, bump the front of the comb with the heel of the hand to start it.

2. Partially open the lever to give access to the hammer spring screw and strain screw, at the rear of the lower tang. Loosening the strain screw will make removal of the spring screw easier, but this is not absolutely necessary. After removal of the spring screw, disengage the spring hooks from the hammer stirrup, and take out the hammer spring toward the rear.

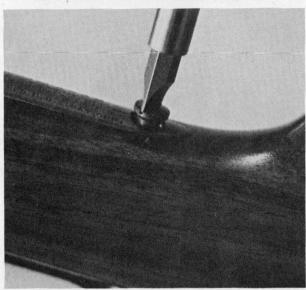

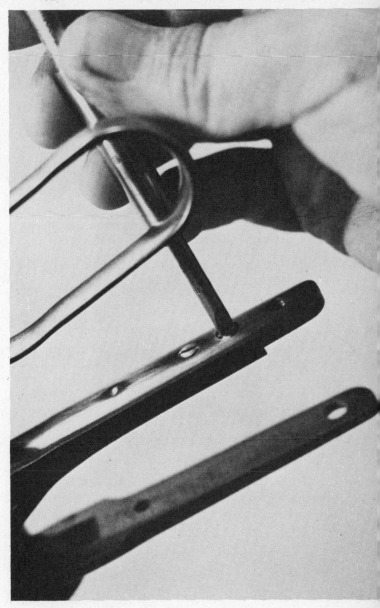

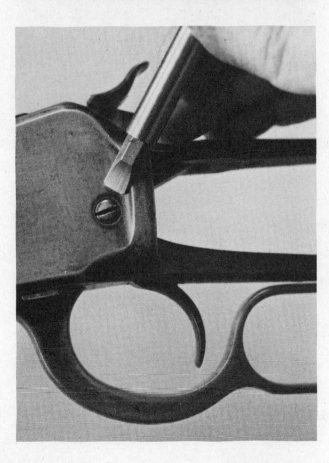

3. Remove the cross-screw on the left side at the rear of the receiver that retains the hammer and the lower tang/trigger housing unit. Pulling the trigger to relieve its spring tension on the hammer will make removal of the screw easier.

4. Hold the trigger to the rear, and remove the hammer upward and toward the rear.

5. The lower tang/trigger housing unit may now be slid out toward the rear. If the unit is very tight, insert a bronze or aluminum rod through the spring screw hole, which has no threads (**not** the stock screw hole), and tap the rod to start the unit out. Drifting out the cross-pin in the lower tang unit will allow removal of the trigger downward.

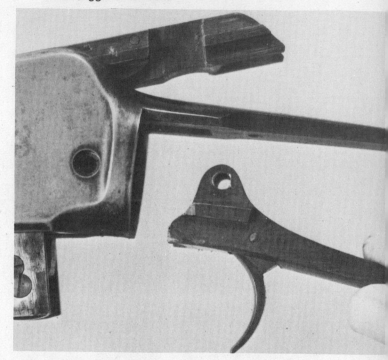

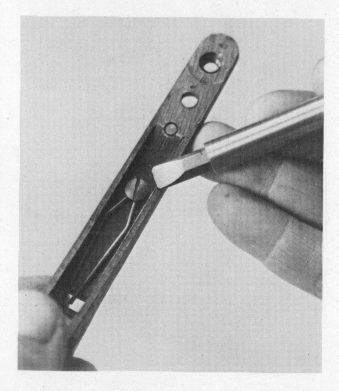

6. The trigger spring is retained by a vertical screw inside the lower tang, and the spring is removed upward. The one shown has a round wire spring, but early guns will have a blade type.

8. The part above the screw, although slotted, is not a screw. It is the cross-pin that links the locking blocks to the lever. Push out the cross-pin toward the left. Then remove the right and left locking blocks downward.

7. With the lever opened, remove the lock screw in the left locking block, the screw nearest its lower edge.

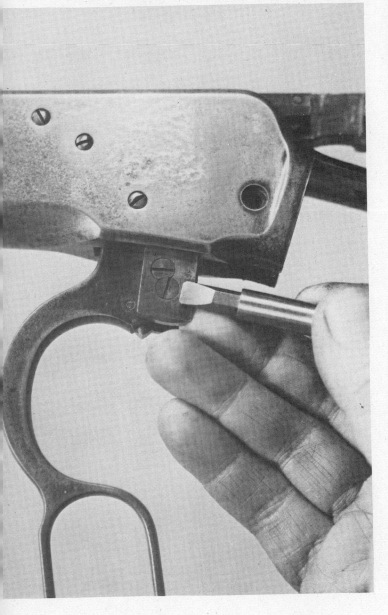

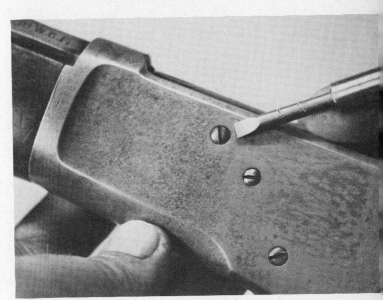

9. Remove the lever pin cover screw, located on the left side of the receiver at the upper front.

10. Move the breechblock (bolt) to the fully closed position, and insert one of the locking blocks from below to hold it in place. Insert a drift punch into the access hole on the right side of the receiver, and push out the lever/bolt connecting pin toward the left. Remove the lever downward and toward the rear.

11. Drifting out the cross-pin in the base of the lever will allow removal of the lever latch plunger and its spring toward the rear. **Caution:** *This is a strong little spring, and it is under tension, so control it and ease it out.*

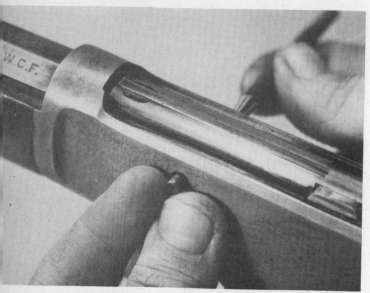

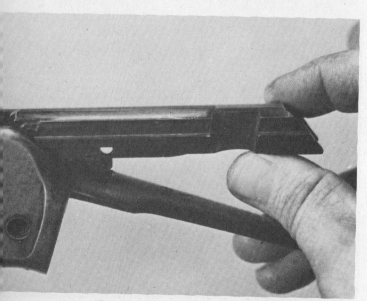

12. Remove the temporarily inserted locking block, and take out the breechblock toward the rear.

13. Removal of the lever pin will also have freed the ejector and its collar and spring, and these can now be taken out of the breechblock toward the front.

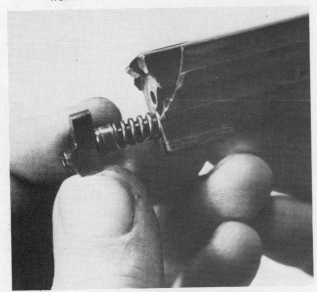

14. Drifting out the smaller cross-pin near the top of the bolt will allow removal of the extractor.

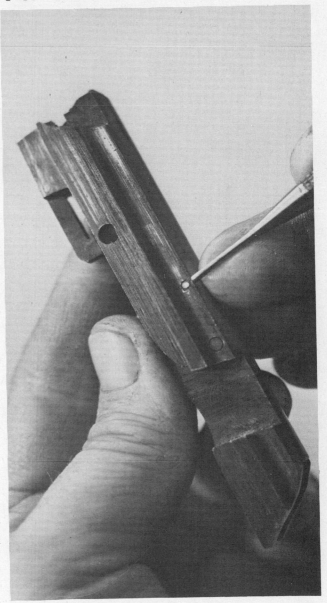

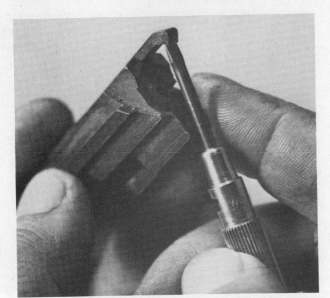

15. After the pin is drifted out, do **not** lift the extractor upward, as this may break its tempered tail. Hook a small screwdriver under the forward beak of the extractor, and lever it straight out toward the front.

16. Drift out the larger of the two cross-pins in the bolt, the firing pin retaining pin, and take out the firing pin toward the rear.

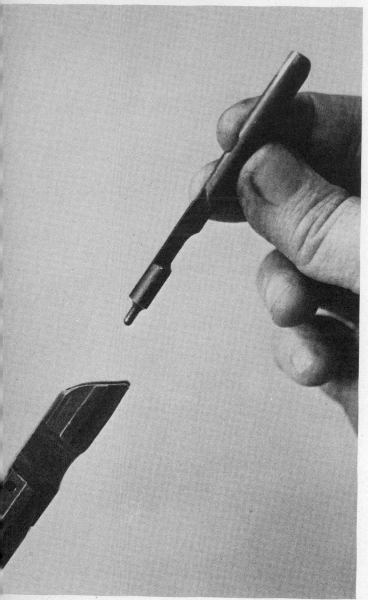

17. Remove the carrier screws, one on each side of the receiver.

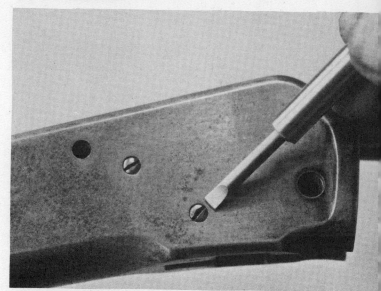

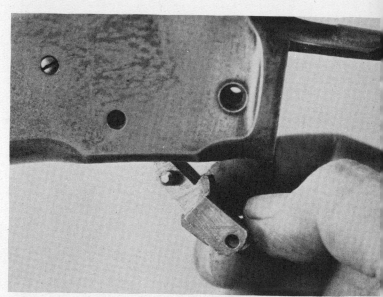

18. After the screws are removed, move the carrier toward the rear, and take it out downward. Note that the carrier plunger may jump into one of the screw holes during removal, and a drift punch will then have to be inserted to depress the plunger and free it.

19. The carrier plunger and its spring are retained in the carrier by a vertical pin. The spring is under tension, so restrain the plunger during removal.

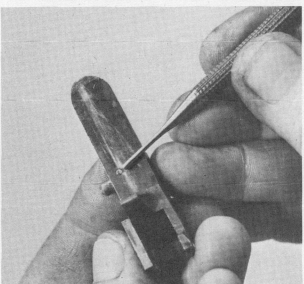

20. Removal of the cartridge guide screws, one on each side, will release the guides to be taken out of the inside of the receiver. The left guide has the cartridge stop mounted on a vertical pin at its forward end, and the cartridge stop spring is in a recess in the back of the guide. The spring is freed by removal of the guide mounting screw, so take care that it isn't lost during removal of the guide.

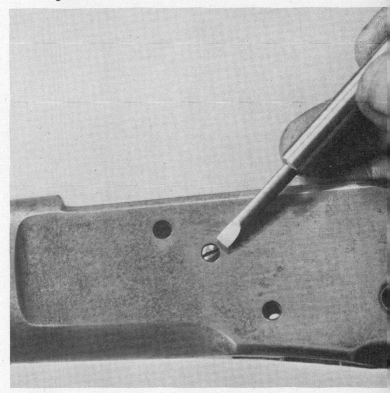

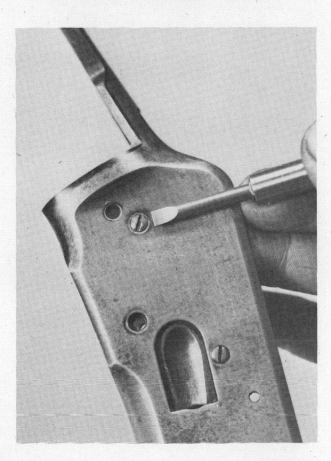

21. The loading gate is its own spring, and is retained by a screw on the right side, near the rear of the receiver. After removal of the screw, the gate is easily taken out.

22. Removal of the screw on the underside of the magazine tube near the muzzle will allow the end plug, magazine spring, and magazine follower to be taken out toward the front. **Note:** Some magazine springs have more tension than others. To be safe, restrain the end plug and ease it out.

23. Remove the screws on each side of the fore-end cap, and move the cap forward along the magazine tube.

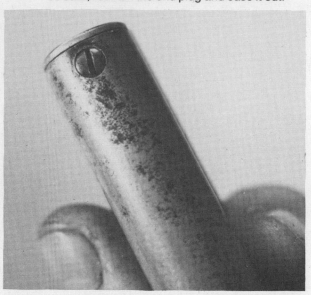

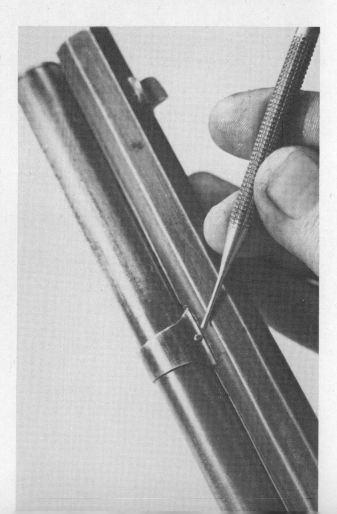

24. Drift out the small cross-pin in the magazine tube hanger loop, and remove the magazine tube toward the front. The fore-end is now moved forward, then downward and off.

Reassembly Tips:

1. When replacing the carrier in the receiver, it will be necessary to insert a small screwdriver to depress the carrier plunger to clear the inner frame wall at the rear.

2. When replacing the ejector in the front of the bolt, note that the collar goes at the rear of the spring, to contact the spring base hook below the bolt. Keep the receiver slanted upward during insertion of the bolt, to prevent the ejector assembly from dropping out.

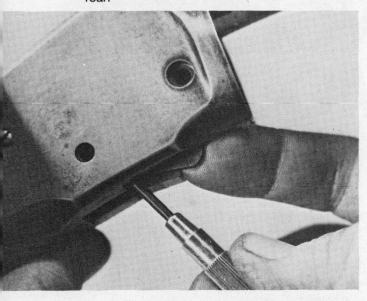

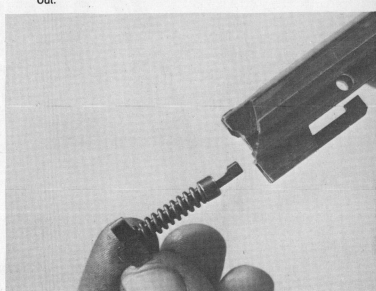

When replacing the lever and its bolt connector pin, once again insert a locking block from below, to hold the bolt in full forward position during replacement of the pin. Also, note that the pin is beveled on one end, and this end should be inserted.

When replacing the left cartridge guide, be sure the cartridge stop spring is properly in place in its recess, with its forward tip hooked beneath the rear tab of the cartridge stop, and the concave side of the spring toward the inner wall of the receiver.

3. When replacing the locking blocks in the receiver, remember that the one with the lock screw goes on the left side.

WINCHESTER MODEL 94

Data:	Winchester Model 94
Origin:	United States
Manufacturer:	Winchester Repeating Arms Company New Haven, Connecticut
Cartridge:	30-30 Winchester
Magazine capacity:	6 rounds
Over-all length:	37¾ inches
Barrel length:	20 inches
Weight:	6½ pounds

To say that this gun needs no introduction would be an understatement. However, since some younger readers might not have been with us long enough to have learned its history, let's briefly pass along the information that it was designed by John M. Browning, and has been produced continuously by Winchester since 1894. It was originally chambered for two blackpowder loads, but for most of its production life the calibers have been the 30-30 and 32 Winchester Special, the latter recently discontinued. There have been several slight internal design changes along the way, but the instructions will generally apply to all 94s.

Disassembly:

1. Use a screwdriver with a wide, thin blade to remove the lever pin cover screw, located on the left side of the receiver at the upper front.

2. Use a drift punch to push out the lever pin toward the left. This is accessible through a small hole on the right side of the receiver, just above the front of the loading gate.

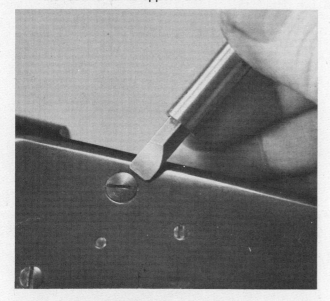

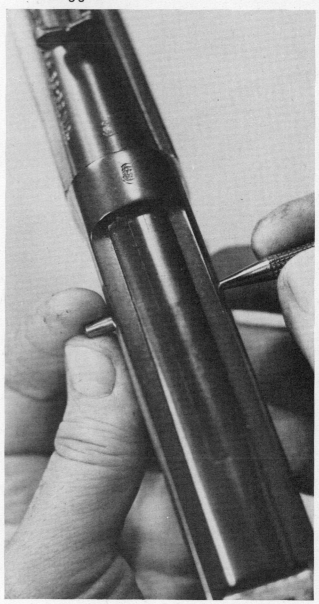

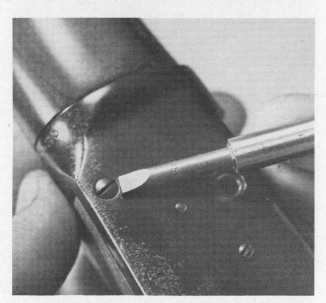

3. Remove the cross-screw that pivots the link plate at the lower left front of the receiver.

4. Move the lever downward, along with the attached link, then move them forward, disengaging the rear of the link from the locking block. The lever and link assembly are then removed downward.

5. Drifting out the large cross-pin in the link plate will release the lever for removal. Drifting out the small cross-pin at the rear of the link plate will release the plate latch plunger and its spring toward the rear. The spring is under tension, so restrain the plunger and ease it out.

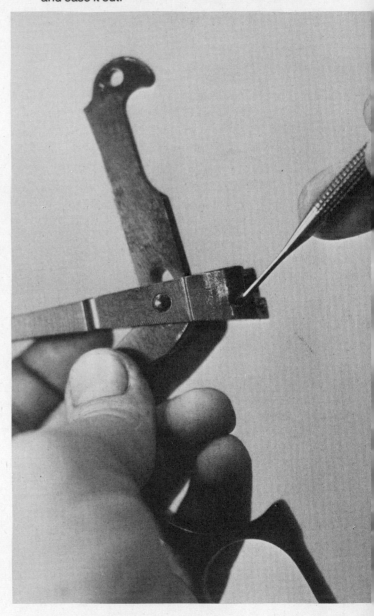

6. Remove the carrier pivot screw toward the left. Note that on early guns, there are two separate screws, one on each side of the receiver.

7. Remove the carrier downward.

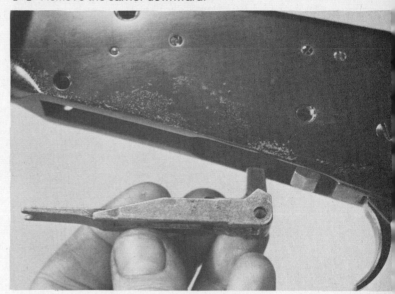

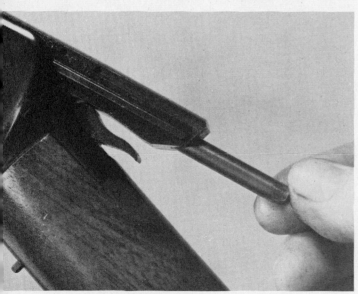

8. It should be noted that removal of the lever will have released the firing pin (in late guns), and if it needs to be taken out for repair, this can be done without further disassembly. In early guns, a firing pin retaining pin at the lower rear of the bolt must also be removed. Also, the extractor can be taken out by moving the bolt to the rear and drifting out its cross-pin or cross-pins (later guns have two).

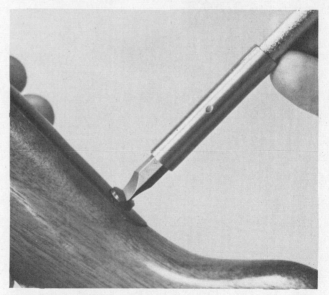

9. Remove the vertical screw at the rear of the upper tang, and take off the stock toward the rear. If the stock is tightly fitted, bump the front of the comb with the heel of the hand to start it.

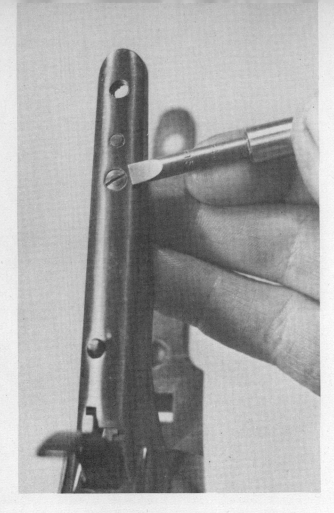

10. With the hammer lowered to the fired position, remove the hammer spring screw, located on the inside of the lower tang at the rear. This will be made easier by first backing out or removing the hammer spring strain screw, as shown.

11. Removal of the hammer spring screw will require an offset screwdriver, or one with an angled tip, as shown. After the screw is removed, the spring and its angled base are taken out toward the rear.

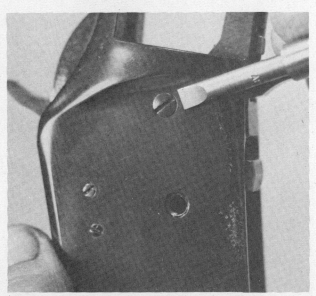

12. Remove the cross-screw that retains both the hammer and the lower tang/trigger housing. Remove the hammer upward and toward the rear.

13. Remove the lower tang/trigger housing unit toward the rear. If this assembly is tight, use a drift punch of nylon or some other non-marring material to nudge it out.

14. The locking block can now be removed downward. Drifting out the roll cross-pin near the top of the locking block will allow removal of the short firing pin striker.

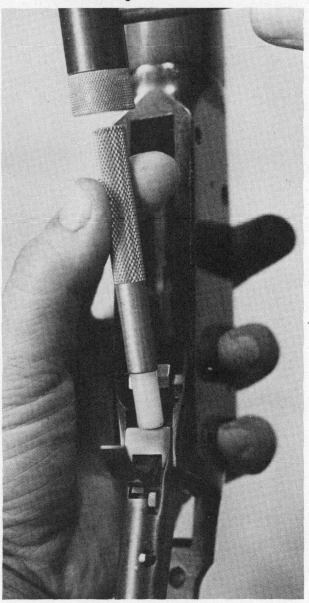

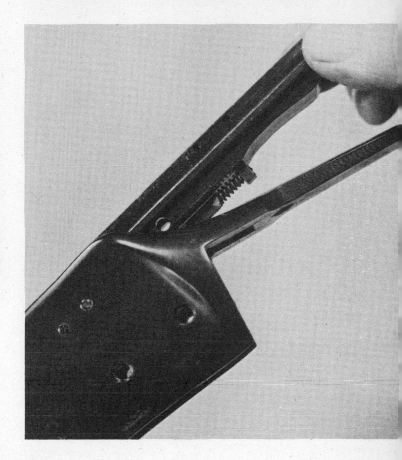

15. The breechblock (bolt) can now be moved straight out of the receiver toward the rear.

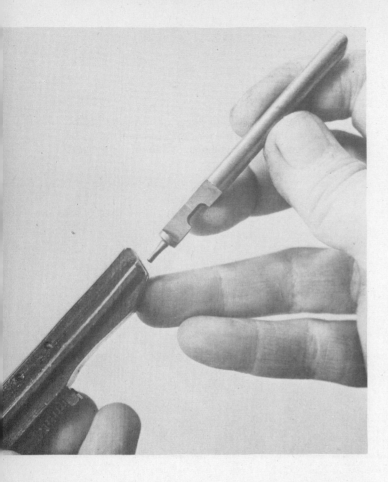

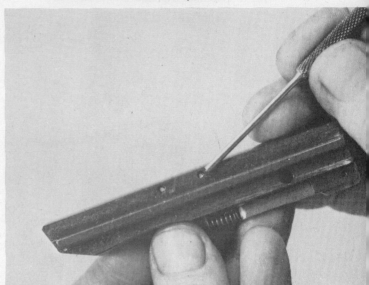

16. If it has not been previously removed, the firing pin can now be taken out of the bolt toward the rear. In early guns, a small retaining cross-pin at the lower rear of the bolt must be driven out to release the firing pin.

17. The extractor is retained in the top of the bolt by a single solid cross-pin (early guns), or by two roll cross-pins (late guns). After these are drifted out, the extractor is removed upward.

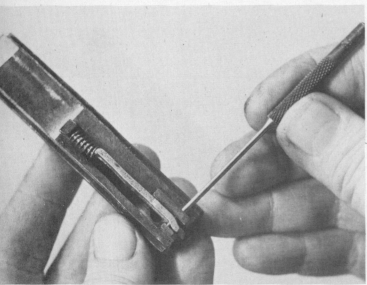

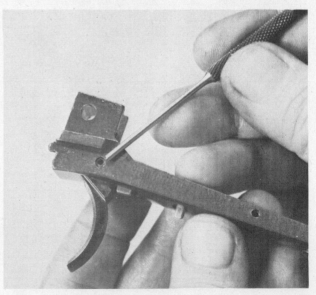

18. The ejector and its spring are retained on the underside of the bolt by a single cross-pin at the lower front. Use a roll pin drift to remove the pin, and take out the ejector and its spring toward the front.

19. The trigger and sear are retained in the trigger housing by a roll cross-pin that is the pivot for both parts. After the pin is drifted out, the trigger is removed downward, the sear toward the front.

20. A cross-pin at the center of the lower tang unit retains both the trigger stop and the combination spring that powers the stop and the sear. Drift out the pin toward the left, so the spring will be released first.

21. Remove the screw on the right side of the receiver directly to the rear of the loading gate, and take out the loading gate from inside the receiver.

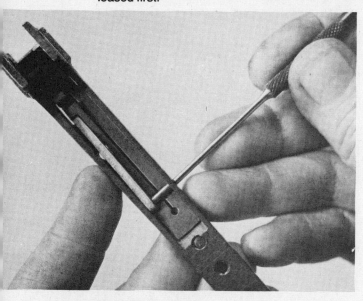

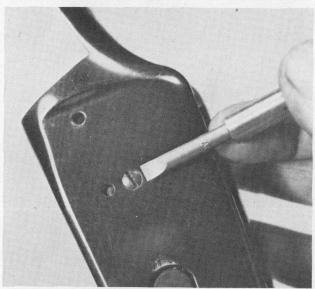

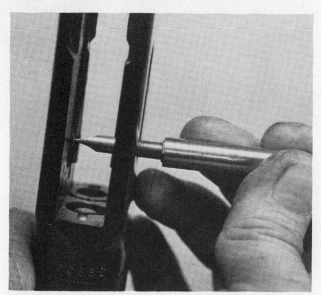

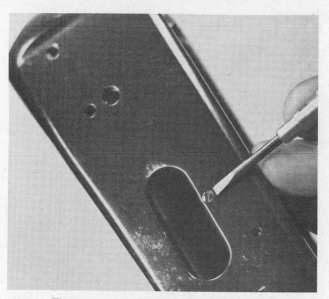

22. With the loading gate removed, the screw that retains the carrier spring will be accessible through the front portion of the loading port. Remove the screw, and take out the spring from inside the receiver.

23. There are two small screws, one on each side of the receiver, the one on the right being just above the loading port. These retain the right and left cartridge guides inside the receiver. In normal takedown, these are best left in place, as any slight misalignment during reassembly can cause problems, one of which is possible stripping of the screws.

24. Removal of the vertical screw at the forward end of the magazine tube will allow the magazine plug, magazine spring, and follower to be taken out toward the front. **Caution:** *The magazine spring is under some tension, so control it and ease it out.*

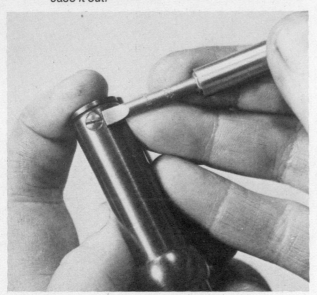

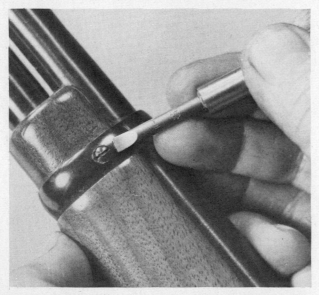

25. Remove the cross-screw from the front barrel band. Remove the cross-screw from the rear barrel band, and slide the barrel band forward, off the front of the fore-end wood. The magazine tube can now be moved out toward the front, and the fore-end can be moved slightly forward and taken off downward.

Reassembly Tips:

1. When replacing the locking block in the receiver, note that the upper wings of the block must be toward the rear.

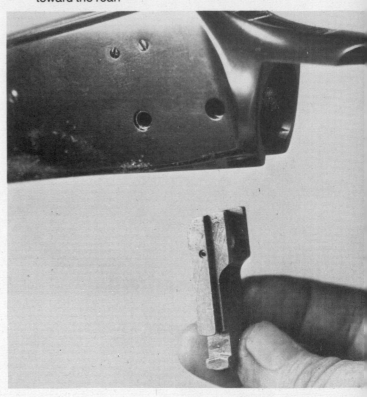

When replacing the firing pin in the breechblock, note that it must be oriented for insertion of the lever, with its front recess on the left side—see step number 16.

When replacing the loading gate, hold it in position inside the receiver with a fingertip, centering the hole for insertion of the screw. To align the screw for proper start, allow the front tip of the gate to protrude from the loading port. As soon as the screw is started, though, be sure to depress the front of the gate inside the port before tightening the screw.